Practice Book

Grade 1

SCHOOL PUBLISHERS

Visit *The Learning Site*!
www.harcourtschool.com

Printed in the United States of America

ISBN 10: 0-15-379503-4
ISBN 13: 978-0-15-379503-9

11 12 13 14 15   0982   16 15
4500527503

Contents

LEAD THE WAY—BOOK 1-1

Practice Book
© Harcourt • Grade 1

JOYFUL NOISE—BOOK 1-5

Practice Book
© Harcourt • Grade 1

Lead the Way

Book 1-1

Name _____

▶ **Say the letter names. Trace the letters.
Then write the letters.**

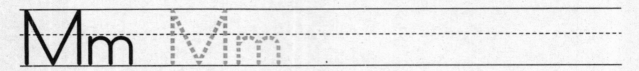

▶ **Say the picture name. Listen for the sound for the
letter <u>m</u>. Do you hear the sound at the beginning or
the end? Write <u>m</u> on one of the lines to show.**

1.

2.

3.

4.

5.

6.

7.

8.

9.

Practice Book
© Harcourt • Grade 1 • Get Started Lesson 1

Name _____

▶ **Say the letter names. Trace the letters. Then write the letters.**

Ss Ss _____

▶ **Say the picture name. Listen for the sound for the letter s. Do you hear the sound at the beginning or the end? Write s on one of the lines to show.**

1. 	2. 	3.
4.	5. 	6. 
7.	8. 	9. 

▶ **Say the letter names. Trace the letters. Then write the letters.**

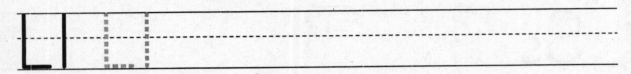

▶ **Say the picture name. Listen for the sound for the letter l. Do you hear the sound at the beginning or the end? Write l on one of the lines to show.**

1.

2.

3.

4.

5.

6.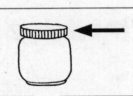

7.

8.

9.

▶ **Say the letter names. Trace the letters.**
Then write the letters.

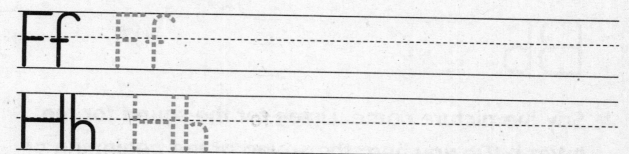

▶ **Say the picture name. Write _f_ or _h_ for the beginning sound.**

Practice Book
© Harcourt • Grade 1 • Get Started Lesson 1

Name _____

▶ **Say the letter names. Trace the letters. Then write the letters.**

Bb Bb _____

▶ **Say the picture name. Listen for the sound for the letter _b_. Do you hear the sound at the beginning or the end? Write _b_ on one of the lines to show.**

1.

_____

_ _ _ _ _ _ _ _ _ _ _ _ _ _

_____

2.

_____

_ _ _ _ _ _ _ _ _ _ _ _ _ _

_____

3.

_____

_ _ _ _ _ _ _ _ _ _ _ _ _ _

_____

4.

_____

_ _ _ _ _ _ _ _ _ _ _ _ _ _

_____

5.

_____

_ _ _ _ _ _ _ _ _ _ _ _ _ _

_____

6.

_____

_ _ _ _ _ _ _ _ _ _ _ _ _ _

_____

7.

_____

_ _ _ _ _ _ _ _ _ _ _ _ _ _

_____

8.

_____

_ _ _ _ _ _ _ _ _ _ _ _ _ _

_____

9.

_____

_ _ _ _ _ _ _ _ _ _ _ _ _ _

_____

Name _____

▶ **Say the letter names. Trace the letters. Then write the letters.**

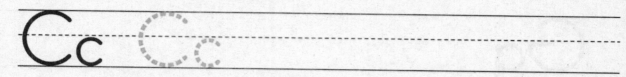

▶ **Say the first picture name. Write <u>c</u> to show that the name begins with the sound for the letter <u>c</u>. Say the other picture names. Color the pictures whose names begin with the sound for <u>c</u>.**

Practice Book
© Harcourt • Grade 1 • Get Started Lesson 1

▶ **Say the letter names. Trace the letters.**
Then write the letters.

▶ **Say the picture name. Listen for the sound for the**
letter g. Do you hear the sound at the beginning or
the end? Write g on one of the lines to show.

1. 	**2.** 	**3.** 
4. 	**5.**	**6.**
7. 	**8.**	**9.**

Name _____

▶ **Say the letter names. Trace the letters. Then write the letters.**

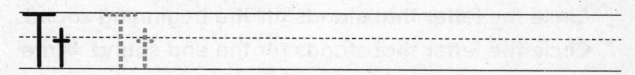

▶ **Say the picture name. Listen for the sound for the letter t. Do you hear the sound at the beginning or the end? Write t on one of the lines to show.**

1.

2.

3.

4.

5.

6.

7.

8.

9.

Practice Book
© Harcourt • Grade 1 • Get Started Lesson 1

Name _____

▶ **Look at the letters above the picture.**
Say the picture name. Listen for the letter-sounds.
Circle the letter that stands for the beginning sound.
Circle the letter that stands for the end sound. Write
the letters on the lines.

1. c m h t

_____   _____
- - - - -   - - - - -
_____   _____

2. t s l b

_____   _____
- - - - -   - - - - -
_____   _____

3. f s b g

_____   _____
- - - - -   - - - - -
_____   _____

4. l t c m

_____   _____
- - - - -   - - - - -
_____   _____

5. g b s l

_____   _____
- - - - -   - - - - -
_____   _____

6. h f t c

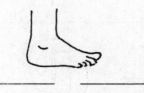

_____   _____
- - - - -   - - - - -
_____   _____

7. b l h t

_____   _____
- - - - -   - - - - -
_____   _____

8. f l h g

_____   _____
- - - - -   - - - - -
_____   _____

9. g s f b

_____   _____
- - - - -   - - - - -
_____   _____

Practice Book
© Harcourt • Grade 1 • Get Started Lesson 1

▶ **Look at the letters above the picture.**
Say the picture name. Listen for the letter-sounds.
Circle the letter that stands for the beginning sound.
Circle the letter that stands for the end sound. Write
the letters on the lines.

I. b s c g

_____ _____
- - - - - - - -   - - - - - - - -

2. t m l h

_____ _____
- - - - - - - -   - - - - - - - -

3. g c s t

_____ _____
- - - - - - - -   - - - - - - - -

4. c t f m

_____ _____
- - - - - - - -   - - - - - - - -

5. t b h l

_____ _____
- - - - - - - -   - - - - - - - -

6. h f t s

_____ _____
- - - - - - - -   - - - - - - - -

7. g b f m

_____ _____
- - - - - - - -   - - - - - - - -

8. g b l h

_____ _____
- - - - - - - -   - - - - - - - -

9. b g c t

_____ _____
- - - - - - - -   - - - - - - - -

▶ **Say the letter names. Trace the letters.**
Then write the letters.

▶ **Say the picture name. Listen for the sound for the**
letter _d_. Do you hear the sound at the beginning or
the end? Write _d_ on one of the lines to show.

1.

2.

3.

4.

5.

6.

7.

8.

9.

Practice Book

© Harcourt • Grade 1 • Get Started Lesson 2

Name _____

▶ **Say the letter names. Trace the letters. Then write the letters.**

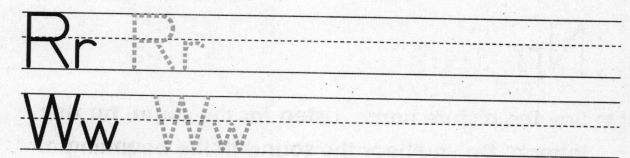

R r

W w

▶ **Say the picture name. Write r or w for the beginning sound.**

1.

2.

3.

4.

5.

6.

7.

8.

9.

10.

11.

12.

GS12

Practice Book
© Harcourt • Grade 1 • Get Started Lesson 2

Name _____

▶ **Say the letter names. Trace the letters. Then write the letters.**

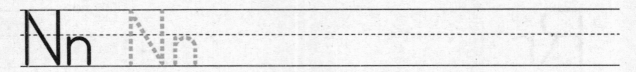

▶ **Say the picture name. Listen for the sound for the letter n. Do you hear the sound at the beginning or the end? Write n on one of the lines to show.**

1.

2.

3.

4.

5.

6.

7.

8.

9.

Practice Book

© Harcourt • Grade 1 • Get Started Lesson 2

Name _____

▶ **Say the letter names. Trace the letters. Then write the letters.**

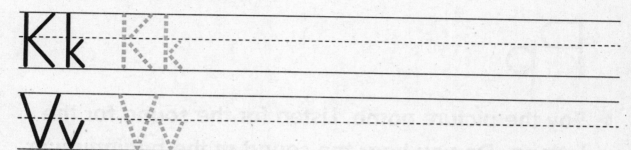

▶ **Say the picture name. Write k or v for the beginning sound.**

1.

2.

3.

4.

5.

6.

7.

8.

9.

10.

11.

12.

GS14

Practice Book
© Harcourt • Grade 1 • Get Started Lesson 2

Name _____

▶ **Say the letter names. Trace the letters.
Then write the letters.**

P p   P p

▶ **Say the picture name. Listen for the sound for the
letter _p_. Do you hear the sound at the beginning or
the end? Write _p_ on one of the lines to show.**

1.

2.

3.

4.

5.

6.

7.

8.

9.

GS15

Practice Book

Name _____

▶ **Say the letter names. Trace the letters. Then write the letters.**

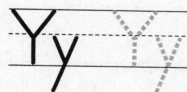

▶ **Say the first picture name. Write y to show that the name begins with the sound for the letter y. Say the other three picture names. Color the picture whose name begins with the sound for y.**

1.

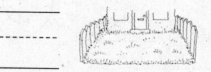  

2.

3.

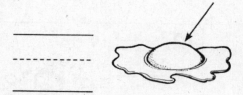   

GS16

▶ **Say the letter names. Trace the letters.**
Then write the letters.

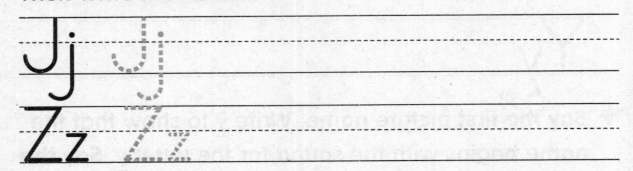

▶ **Say the picture name. Write j or z for the beginning sound.**

1.

2.

3.

4.

5.

6.

7.

8.

9.

10.

11.

12.

Practice Book
© Harcourt • Grade 1 • Get Started Lesson 3

Name _____

▶ **Say the letter names. Trace the letters. Then write the letters.**

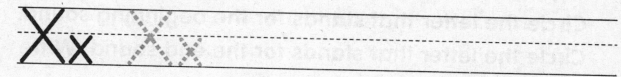

▶ **Say the first picture name. Write x to show that the name ends with the sounds for the letter x. Say the other three picture names. Color the picture whose name ends with the sounds for x.**

1.

 _____

2.

_____

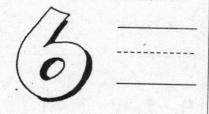   

3.

_____

GS18

▶ **Look at the letters above the picture.**
Say the picture name. Listen for the letter-sounds.
Circle the letter that stands for the beginning sound.
Circle the letter that stands for the end sound. Write
the letters on the lines.

1. c   d   g   z

_____   _____

2. p   b   n   x

_____   _____

3. y   j   w   n

_____   _____

4. w   r   m   p

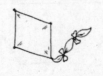

_____   _____

5. b   x   d   v

_____   _____

6. f   j   d   g

_____   _____

7. k   y   h   t

_____   _____

8. s   z   p   l

_____   _____

9. f   v   j   n

_____   _____

▶ **Look at the letters above the picture.**
Say the picture name. Listen for the letter-sounds.
Circle the letter that stands for the beginning sound.
Circle the letter that stands for the end sound. Write
the letters on the lines.

1. m   n   w   x

_____   _____
- - - - - - - -   - - - - - - - -
_____   _____

2. r   h   d   p

_____   _____
- - - - - - - -   - - - - - - - -

3. r   k   n   z

_____   _____
- - - - - - - -   - - - - - - - -

4. b   p   v   n

_____   _____
- - - - - - - -   - - - - - - - -
_____   _____

5. v   l   x   s

_____   _____
- - - - - - - -   - - - - - - - -

6. y   n   j   t

_____   _____
- - - - - - - -   - - - - - - - -

7. y   w   k   g

_____   _____
- - - - - - - -   - - - - - - - -

8. v   d   t   p

_____   _____
- - - - - - - -   - - - - - - - -

9. f   k   x   j

_____   _____
- - - - - - - -   - - - - - - - -

Name _____

Phonics:
Digraph /ch/*ch*,
Trigraph /ch/*tch*

Lesson 13

▶ **Circle the word that completes each sentence. Then write the word.**

branch · **brush** **brand**

_____

I. The cat sits on a _____ .

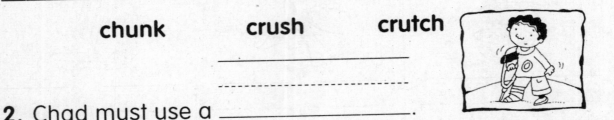

chunk **crush** **crutch**

_____

----

2. Chad must use a _____ .

best **bent** **bench**

_____

----

3. We sit on the _____ to eat.

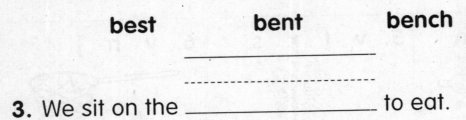

catch **chest** **chunk**

_____

----

4. My doll is in the _____ .

desk **ditch** **dish**

_____

----

5. The dog is in the _____ .

School–Home Connection

Have your child read the sentences aloud.
Together, think of more words with *ch* or *tch*.

2

Practice Book

Name _____

▶ **Read the Spelling Words. Then write each word in the group where it belongs.**

Words with <u>a</u>

_____   _____

_____   _____

_____   _____

_____   _____

_____   _____

_____   _____

_____   _____

_____   _____

_____

Spelling Words

am

at

cat

can

ran

man

map

tap

a

the

Word without <u>a</u>

_____

_____

School–Home Connection

Have your child read each Spelling Word aloud. Talk about how the words are alike and how they are different.

3

Practice Book
© Harcourt • Grade 1 • Book 1

Name _____

▶ **Circle the word that completes each sentence. Then write the word.**

mat   hat

_____

----

1. Jan has a _____.

fan   nap

_____

----

2. Max had a _____.

ran   sat

_____

----

3. Pam _____.

lad   sad

_____

----

4. I am _____.

cat   can

_____

----

5. He has a _____.

School–Home Connection

Have your child read the words and sentences
aloud. Ask him or her to write other words
with the short a sound.

4

▶ **Write the word that best completes each sentence.**

man	now	mad

_____
- - - - - - - - - -
1. Max can bat _____ .

help	ham	hat

_____
- - - - - - - - - -
2. Dad can _____ Max.

Lap	Let's	Lab

_____
- - - - - - - - - -
3. _____ see Max go!

School–Home Connection

Have your child read each sentence aloud.
Ask your child to say these words in other
sentences: *now, help, let's.*

5

▶ **Read the sentences. Draw a line from the sentences to the picture that shows what will happen next.**

1. Jan can bat.
　　She can bat now. ●　　　　●

2. I have a rag.
　　I go to the van. ●　　　　●

3. Pat ran.
　　Pat ran a lap. ●　　　　●

Practice Book
© Harcourt • Grade 1 • Book 1

▶ **Write the word that completes the sentence.**

1. Dan has _____.

cat
cats

_____

2. I see two _____.

bat
bats

_____

3. Jan _____ Max.

tag
tags

_____

4. The cat _____.

nap
naps

_____

5. There are two _____.

van
vans

School–Home Connection
Have your child read the words and sentences aloud to you.

7

▶ **Add words to make each word or group of words into a sentence. Write the sentences correctly.**

1. ran

_____

- -

_____

_____

2. we

_____

- -

_____

_____

3. the cat

_____

- -

_____

_____

4. i like

_____

- -

_____

_____

5. has

_____

- -

_____

School–Home Connection

Have your child create sentences about things he or she can do, and say them aloud. Ask your child to tell how to begin and end each sentence.

8

Practice Book
© Harcourt • Grade 1 • Book 1

▶ **Circle the word that completes the
sentence. Then write the word.**

map   tap

_____
- - - - - - - - - - - - - - - -

1. Pam can _____.

tags   wags

_____
- - - - - - - - - - - - - - - -

2. Jan _____ Dan.

raps   ran

_____
- - - - - - - - - - - - - - - -

3. The cat _____ out.

can   pan

_____
- - - - - - - - - - - - - - - -

4. I want that _____.

am   at

_____
- - - - - - - - - - - - - - - -

5. I _____ a cat.

Name _____

▶ **Read the Spelling Words. Then write each word in the group where it belongs.**

Words with <u>a</u>

_____   _____
_____   _____
_____   _____
_____   _____
_____   _____
_____   _____

Words without <u>a</u>

_____   _____

Spelling
Words

hat
had
sad
sat
bat
bag
at
can
help
now

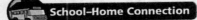
School–Home Connection

Ask your child to change the last letter in the word *hat* to make another Spelling Word (*had*). Repeat this activity with the words *sad* (*sat*) and *bat* (*bag*).

10

▶ **Write the word from the box that completes each sentence**

| sad | ran | cat | can |

_____

1. I see a _____.

_____

2. Pat has a _____.

_____

3. She _____.

_____

4. I am _____.

School–Home Connection

Have your child read the word choices and
each sentence aloud. Talk about what is
happening in the pictures.

11

▶ **Write the word that best completes
the sentence.**

an   in   up

_____

- - - - - - - - - - - - -

1. I look _____ the pan.

---

no   nap   do

_____

- - - - - - - - - - - - -

2. I see _____ ham.

---

tap   tan   too

_____

- - - - - - - - - - - - -

3. I want ham, _____.

School–Home Connection

Have your child read each word and sentence
aloud. Encourage your child to write the words
in, *no*, and *too* in other sentences.

12

Practice Book
© Harcourt • Grade 1 • Book 1

▶ **Read the story. Look at the picture.**
Circle the sentence that tells what
will happen next.

1. My cat ran to me.
My cat sat in my lap.

My cat has a nap.   My cat looks at a van.

2. Jan looks at a map.
Pam sat down.

Pam ran out.   Pam looks at the map.

3. I have two bats.
Dan wants a bat.

I give Dan one bat.   Dan gives me a bat.

School–Home Connection

Have your child read the sentences aloud. Talk
about how the pictures relate to the words.
Ask your child what else could happen next
based on the story.

13

▶ **Circle the word that completes the
sentence. Then write the word.**

bag   band

_____

- - - - - - - - - - - -

1. I am in a _____ .

tag   hand

_____

- - - - - - - - - - - -

2. I see the _____ .

wag   and

_____

- - - - - - - - - - - -

3. Max _____ Nan are fans.

sag   sand

_____

- - - - - - - - - - - -

4. She sat in the _____ .

rag   land

_____

- - - - - - - - - - - -

5. Give me that _____ .

School–Home Connection

Ask your child to read each sentence aloud.
Then ask him or her to find the words on the
page that rhyme with *bag*. (tag, wag, sag, rag)

14

Name _____

▶ **Write each sentence correctly.**

1. down cat the sat

_____

_____

_____

2. had nap a he

_____

_____

_____

3. in rat a ran

_____

_____

_____

▶ **Write a sentence that tells what happens next.**

_____

4. _____

_____

_____

School–Home Connection

Make up simple sentences that use no more than four words. Then say each sentence with the words out of order. Ask your child to say the sentence correctly.

15

Practice Book

▶ **Circle the word that names each picture. Then write the word.**

1.
bib
_____
- - - - - - - - - - - - - - - -
bag
_____
bit

2.
wag
_____
- - - - - - - - - - - - - - - -
win
_____
wig

3.
pad
_____
- - - - - - - - - - - - - - - -
pit
_____
pig

4.
sax
_____
- - - - - - - - - - - - - - - -
six
_____
silk

5.
hat
_____
- - - - - - - - - - - - - - - -
hit
_____
him

6.
lips
_____
- - - - - - - - - - - - - - - -
laps
_____
limps

7.
pill
_____
- - - - - - - - - - - - - - - -
pan
_____
pin

8.
lad
_____
- - - - - - - - - - - - - - - -
lid
_____
lift

School–Home Connection

Point to each word with *i* on this page. Ask
your child to read the word. Then have him or
her say it in a sentence.

16

Name _____

▶ **Read the Spelling Words. Then write each word in the group where it belongs.**

Words with i

_____   _____

-----------------------   -----------------------

_____   _____

-----------------------   -----------------------

_____   _____

-----------------------   -----------------------

_____   _____

Words without i

_____   _____

-----------------------   -----------------------

_____   _____

-----------------------   -----------------------

_____   _____

Spelling Words
in
pin
pig
big
dig
did
had
sat
no
too

School–Home Connection

Write the word *pig* and have your child change
one letter to make another Spelling Word.
(*big, dig, pin*)

17

▶ **Cross out the word that is wrong.**
Write the correct word.

1. My hat is too bag.

_____

- - - - - - - - - - - - - - - - - - - -

_____

2. This hat will fat.

_____

- - - - - - - - - - - - - - - - - - - -

_____

3. My pants have a rap.

_____

- - - - - - - - - - - - - - - - - - - -

_____

4. This will fax it.

_____

- - - - - - - - - - - - - - - - - - - -

_____

5. He ran and had.

_____

- - - - - - - - - - - - - - - - - - - -

_____

6. I ran to ham.

_____

- - - - - - - - - - - - - - - - - - - -

_____

School–Home Connection

Read each sentence with the incorrect word.
Ask your child to listen carefully, and then read
the sentence with the correct word.

18

Practice Book

▶ **Write the word that best completes
each sentence.**

get   go   gift

_____

----

1. Tim will _____ a cat.

_____

see   so   no

_____

----

2. That cat looks _____ sad.

_____

hold   had   hand

_____

----

3. Tim can _____ the cat.

_____

sand   she   soon

_____

----

4. Tim will have the cat _____.

_____

him   home   here

_____

----

5. The cat will have a _____.

School–Home Connection

Have your child read aloud each completed
sentence. Point to the word your child wrote
and ask her or him to say the word in another
sentence.

19

Name _____

▶ **Read the name of each group. Then circle all the things that belong in that group.**

1. They can dig.

2. They go fast.

3. They are big.

4. They can have naps.

Think of other things that can go in each group. Draw pictures.

 School–Home Connection

Together, think of other group names. Then think of things that can go in that group. Together, draw pictures of things in each group.

Practice Book
© Harcourt • Grade 1 • Book 1

Name _____

▶ **Read the sentences. Write the contraction for the underlined words.**

Where's	What's	He's
Here's	That's	It's

1. <u>Here is</u> the gift.

_____

- - - - - - - - - - - - - - - - - - - -

_____

2. <u>It is</u> a hat.

_____

- - - - - - - - - - - - - - -

_____

3. <u>Where is</u> Dan?

_____

- - - - - - - - - - - - - - - - - - - -

_____

4. <u>He is</u> here now.

_____

- - - - - - - - - - - - - - -

_____

5. <u>What is</u> that?

_____

- - - - - - - - - - - - - - - - - - - -

_____

6. <u>That is</u> a gift for you.

_____

- -

_____

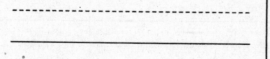

School–Home Connection

Say a simple sentence with one of the
contractions above. Then ask your child
what two words go together to make the
contraction.

21

Name _____

▶ **Add a naming part from the box to complete each sentence.**

| Liz | We | I | Dan |

_____
- - - - - - - - - - - - - - -
1. _____ will go on a raft.

_____
- - - - - - - - - - - - - - -
2. _____ can help lift it.

_____
- - - - - - - - - - - - - - -
3. _____ has a map.

_____
- - - - - - - - - - - - - - -
4. _____ get on.

▶ **Write a sentence that tells what happens next. Write your sentence correctly. Then circle the naming part.**

_____
- -
5. _____

School–Home Connection

Draw a picture with your child. Have your child use complete sentences to tell you what is happening in the picture. Then ask, "Who or what is the sentence about?"

Practice Book

Name _____

▶ Circle the word that names the picture. Then write the word.

1.

tick

tack

_____

task

_____

2.

band

bag

_____

back

_____

3.

lick

lift

_____

lit

_____

4.

sick

sit

_____

sift

_____

5.

cast

kiss

_____

kick

_____

6.

six

sand

_____

sack

_____

 School–Home Connection

Say the following name pairs aloud and ask your child to tell you which names end with the letters ck: Mick, Matt; Jan, Jack; Nate, Nick.

23

Practice Book

Name _____

▶ **Read the Spelling Words. Then write each word in the group where it belongs.**

Words with <u>ck</u>

_____   _____

_____   _____

_____   _____

_____   _____

_____   _____

_____

Words without <u>ck</u>

_____   _____

_____   _____

_____   _____

Spelling Words

pick

pack

tack

back

sack

sick

big

in

hold

so

School–Home Connection

Write the Spelling Words *pack* and *sick*. Have
your child change the second letter in each word
to make another Spelling Word (*pick* and *sack*).

24

Practice Book

Name _____

▶ **Write the word from the box that completes each sentence.**

| Rick | pick | tick | pack | sack |

1. Jack can _____ _____.

2. Pam can _____ _____.

3. _____ has a cat.

4. Dan has a _____ _____.

25

Practice Book

▶ **Write the word that best completes
the sentence.**

lit   late   lack

_____

- - - - - - - - - - - - - - - - - -

I. Dad will get up _____.

_____

One   Oh   Out

_____

- - - - - - - - - - - - - - - - - -

2. _____, Jack! Is this gift for me?

_____

Yap   Yam   Yes

_____

- - - - - - - - - - - - - - - - - -

3. _____, the gift is for you.

26

▶ **Read the story. Then number the pictures in story order.**

Cat has a big hat.

_____
- - - - - - -
_____

Cat has to go back home.

_____
- - - - - - -
_____

Here comes a big wind.

_____
- - - - - - -
_____

27

Practice Book

▶ **Write the word from the box that completes each sentence.**

fill	hit	hill	lit	will	sit

1. Nick and I _____ up the bags.

2. We _____ in the sand.

3. Let's go up the _____.

4. Nick _____ it to me.

5. I _____ go get it.

School–Home Connection

Ask your child to read each sentence aloud.
Together, think of other words that end with *ill*
or *it*. Encourage your child to write each word
as you think of them.

28

Practice Book
© Harcourt • Grade 1 • Book 1

▶ **Write two sentences about the characters in the picture. Make sure each sentence is written correctly, with a naming part and a telling part. Underline the telling part.**

1. _____

2. _____

School–Home Connection

Have your child read aloud the sentences. Ask which words *name* who or what the sentence is about. Then ask which words *tell* what they did or *tell* about them.

29

Practice Book

Name _____

▶ **Read the sentences. Circle the sentence that tells about the picture.**

I. Bob sat on a dock.

Bob has a rock.

2. Fox is on a dock.

Fox hid in the box.

3. My dog and I jog fast.

I can dig in the sand.

4. A fox ran.

The dog naps.

5. A cat is soft.

The box is big.

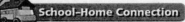

School-Home Connection

Have your child read aloud all the sentences.
Ask which words have the short o vowel sound
as in *mop*.

30

Practice Book

Name _____

▶ **Read the Spelling Words. Then write each word in the group where it belongs.**

Words with o

_____   _____

_____   _____

_____   _____

_____   _____

_____   _____

_____

Spelling Words

top

hop

hot

not

dot

lot

back

pick

oh

yes

Words without o

_____   _____

_____   _____

_____

School–Home Connection

Point to the first six Spelling Words and have your child read them to you. Talk about how the words are alike and how they are different.

31

Name _____

▶ **Look at each picture. Write the word in the box that completes each sentence.**

| pot | job | mom | pond | on | hop |

_____

1. Max can _____ .

_____

2. Jill has a _____ to do.

_____

3. I am at the _____ .

_____

4. Pat and his _____ sit.

_____

5. The mitt is _____ his hand.

_____

6. A ham is in a _____ .

School–Home Connection

Ask your child to read aloud the sentences they
completed. Have them point to the words that
have the short o vowel sound as in *job*.

32

▶ **Circle the word that best completes each sentence. Write the word.**

much   mop   man

_____

- - - - - - - - - - - - - - - - - - - -

1. Jan's pig ran too _____.

fan   fox   find

_____

- - - - - - - - - - - - - - - - - - - -

2. Jan can not _____ the pig.

pond   find · band

_____

- - - - - - - - - - - - - - - - - - - -

3. Tom will _____ Jan's pig.

thank   bank   tank

_____

- - - - - - - - - - - - - - - - - - - -

4. Jan's pig can not _____ Tom.

tank   ink   thank

_____

- - - - - - - - - - - - - - - - - - - -

5. Jan will _____ Tom.

School-Home Connection

Write the word *thank* and let your child read it to you. Talk about a person your child would like to thank for something.

Practice Book

© Harcourt • Grade 1 • Book 1

▶ **Read the sentences. Look at the pictures. Write the word under the picture that tells the character's name.**

1. Cat likes his cap.
   He has a nap in it.

_____
- - - - - - - - - - - - - - - - -
_____

2. Ann got a hit.
   She ran fast.

- - - - - - - - - - - - - - - - -
_____

3. Rob has a gift.
   His gift is in a bag.

_____
- - - - - - - - - - - - - - - - -
_____

4. Jill has a doll. She
   likes the doll.

_____
- - - - - - - - - - - - - - - - -
_____

School–Home Connection
Ask your child to read the sentences aloud.
Talk about the characters.

34

Practice Book
© Harcourt • Grade 1 • Book 1

▶ **Write the word that completes the sentence.**

| locking | honking | lifting |

1. A cab is _____.

| rocked | docked | locked |

2. Liz _____ the cat.

| thanked | added | helped |

3. Dan _____ Mom.

| acting | mixing | camping |

4. We are _____.

Practice Book
© Harcourt • Grade 1 • Book 1

Name _____

▶ **Write these telling sentences correctly.**

1. dogs can dig

_____

_____

2. cats are soft

_____

_____

3. a fox is fast

_____

_____

4. an ant is not big

_____

_____

▶ **Write a telling sentence of your own.**

_____

----

5. _____

School–Home Connection

Have your child create sentences about things in your home, and say them aloud. Ask your child to tell how to begin and end each telling sentence.

36

Practice Book
© Harcourt • Grade 1 • Book 1

▶ **Write the words where they belong in the puzzle.**

| call | wall | fall | ball |

1.

2.

3.

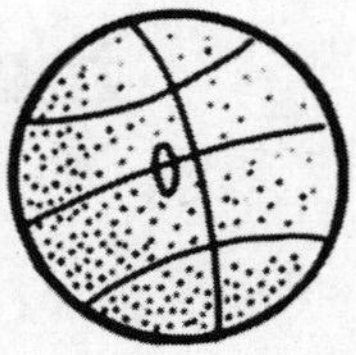

4.

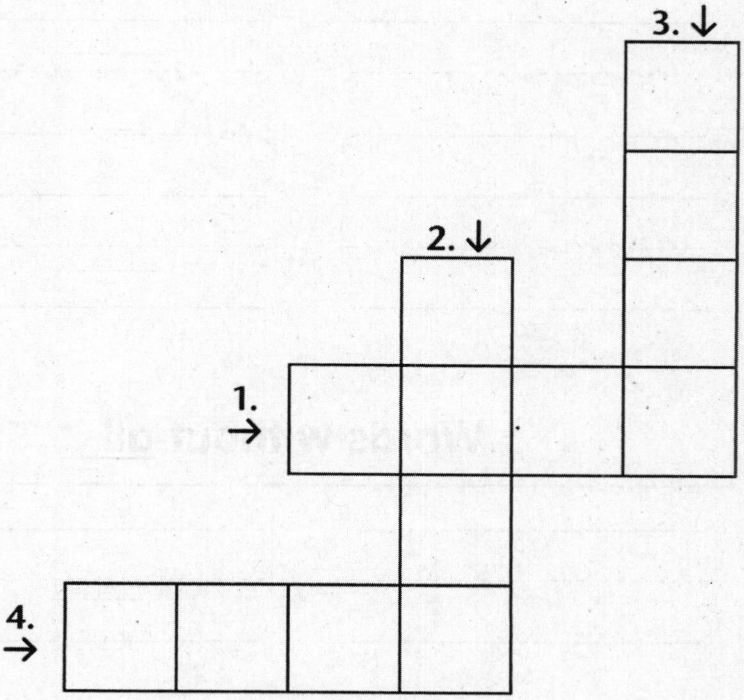

3. ↓

2. ↓

1. →

4. →

Practice Book
© Harcourt • Grade 1 • Book 1

Name _____

▶ **Read the Spelling Words. Then write each word in the group where it belongs.**

Words with <u>all</u>

_____   _____

_____   _____

_____   _____

_____   _____

Words without <u>all</u>

_____   _____

_____   _____

Spelling Words

all
call
fall
wall
ball
tall
not
top
much
thank

School–Home Connection

Have your child read the first six Spelling
Words aloud. Then use those words to make
rhyming sentences.

38

▶ **Circle the word that completes each sentence. Then write the word.**

ball   bill

_____

- - - - - - - - - - - - - -

1. Dad kicks the _____ to Max.

hall   hill

_____

- - - - - - - - - - - - - -

2. Max kicks it down the _____ .

fall   fill

_____

- - - - - - - - - - - - - -

3. Do not _____ , Max!

wall   will

_____

- - - - - - - - - - - - - -

4. Now Jan _____ kick the ball.

all   ill

_____

- - - - - - - - - - - - - -

5. They _____ ran fast to get it.

School–Home Connection

Have your child read each completed sentence
aloud. Talk about how the word choices are
alike and how they are different.

39

▶ **Write the word that best completes the sentence.**

out   of   fox

_____

- - - - - - - - - - - - - - -

1. This is a map _____ the mall.

sand   make   some

_____

- - - - - - - - - - - - - - -

2. I want to get _____ pants.

Hop   How   Had

_____

- - - - - - - - - - - - - - -

3. _____ do they fit?

milk   make   miss

_____

- - - - - - - - - - - - - - -

4. Mom will _____ them fit.

School–Home Connection

Have your child read each completed sentence
aloud. Point to the words *of*, *some*, *How*,
and *make*. Ask your child to say each word in
another sentence.

40

► **Look at the drawings. Think. How are
the animals in each group alike?
Write the word.**

They are	They are
_____	_____
------------------------	------------------------
_____	_____

🪐 **Try This**

Think of other animals. Add one to each group.

 School–Home Connection

Talk about how the pictures are alike and how
they are different. Together, think of other
ways to categorize animals.

Practice Book
© Harcourt • Grade 1 • Book 1

▶ **Complete each sentence. Write the contraction for the two words.**

Dan   is

_____

- - - - - - - - - - - - - - - - -

1. _____ packing a bag.

_____

did   not

_____

- - - - - - - - - - - - - - - - -

2. He _____ have a big bag.

_____

bag   is

_____

- - - - - - - - - - - - - - - - -

3. The _____ filled to the top.

_____

can   not

_____

- - - - - - - - - - - - - - - - -

4. Now he _____ lift it.

School–Home Connection

Have your child read aloud the two words
above each sentence, then read the contraction
he or she used to complete the sentence.

Name _____

▶ **Write each question correctly.**

1. how can he help

_____
- -
_____
_____

2. what can she fix

_____
- -
_____
_____

3. will he fix it

_____
- -
_____
_____

4. who is she

_____
- -
_____
_____

▶ **Write a question about the picture.**

_____
- -
5. _____

School–Home Connection

Have your child think of questions for you to
answer. Help him or her write the questions.
Remind your child to use capital letters and
question marks.

43

Cut-Out/ Fold-Up Books

1

Pam and Cat

— Fold —

3

Cat ran.

— Fold —

8

Pam pats Cat.

6

Here, Cat! Look!

45

4

Now where is Cat?

2

Look!

Come down, Cat!

5

Come down, Cat!

7

Practice Book
© Harcourt • Grade 1 • Book 1 • Cut-Out/Fold-Up Book

Dan and Sam

We like to tap.

3

No! Dan and Sam are pals.

8

Dan and Sam are down!

6

Practice Book
© Harcourt • Grade 1 • Book 1 • Cut-Out/Fold-Up Book

4

Dan sat. Sam sat, too.

2

Can you tap, Dan?

— Fold —

— Fold —

Dan and Sam ran.

5

Are Dan and Sam mad?

7

48

© Harcourt • Grade 1 • Book 1 • Cut-Out/Fold-Up Book

1

Ann and Max

3

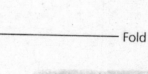

Ann can go.

8

It's Max! It's Ann!
Max and Ann are here!

6

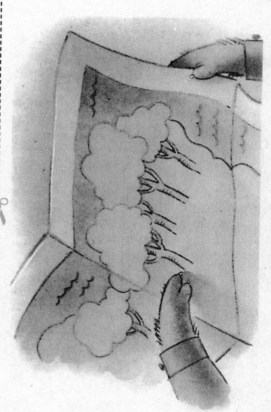

Ann is here.

49

Fold

Fold

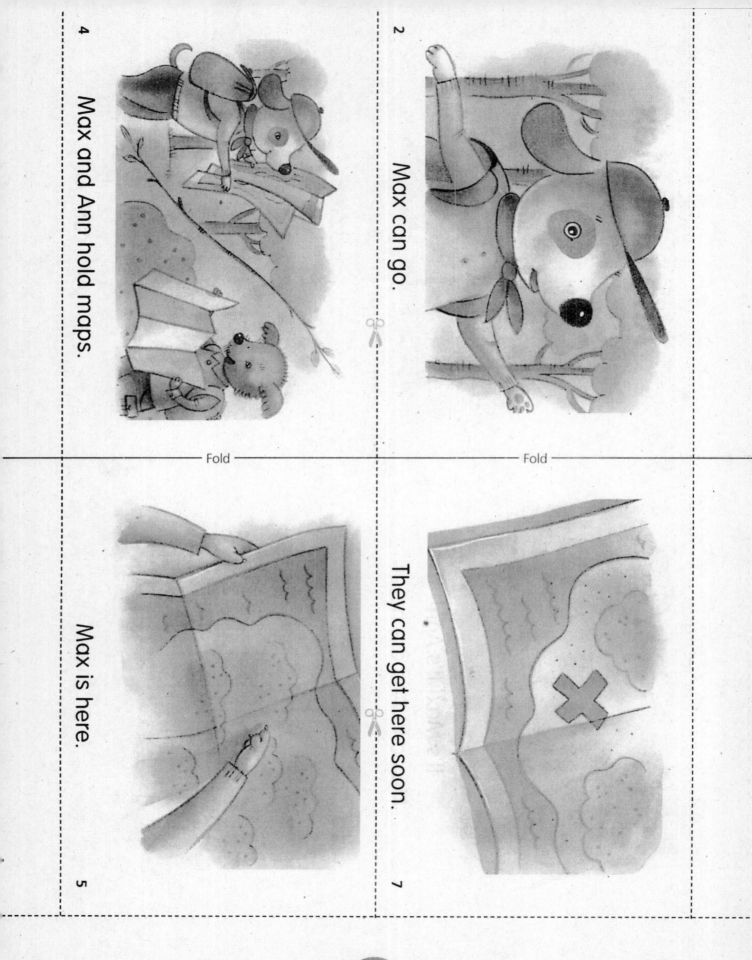

4

Max and Ann hold maps.

2

Max can go.

Max is here.

5

They can get here soon.

7

Jack and Sid

1

Look at what I have, Jack.

3

---- Fold ----

---- Fold ----

Yes! Sid pats him on the back.

8

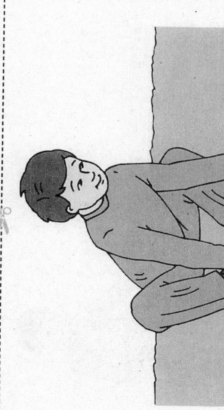

I will help. Sit like I do, Jack.

6

51

4

Oh, Jack! You have it.

— Fold —

2

Sid has a task for Jack.

— Fold —

Now sit, Jack.

5

Will Jack sit, too?

7

What Is In It?

© Harcourt • Grade 1 • Book 1 • Cut-Out/Fold-Up Book

Tim's sack is big, too.

Will he find rocks in it?

Fold   Fold

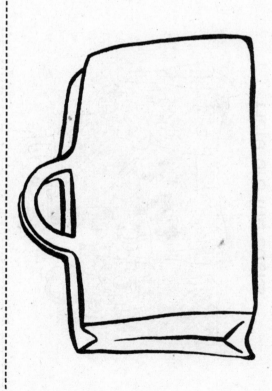

What is in it?

8

Jan has sacks.

The sacks have dots.

6

4

Pat has a little sack.
Not much will fit in it.

2

Liz's sack is big.
What can fit in it?

Fold

Fold

The dog has a sack, too.
Dogs do not pack sacks!

5

Here are the sacks.
Pick the sack for you.

7

54

Thank You, Mom!

1

Where did they all go?

— Fold —

— Fold —

That's how I got it!

8

I see the box here.

6

55

2

Look up on that hill.

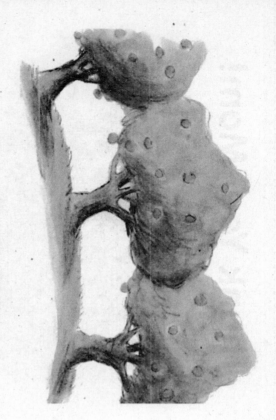

4

A tall man picked some.

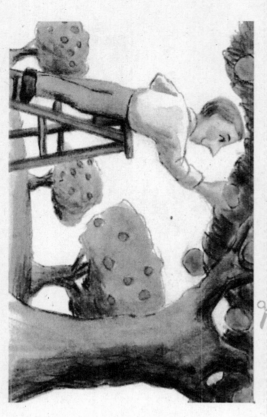

— Fold — — Fold —

He packed some in a box.

5

Mom will help me get one!

7

56

The Lost Dog

Characters

Ann

Tim

Dad

Mom

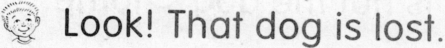 Look! That dog is lost.

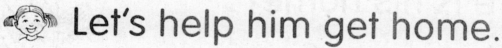 Let's help him get home.

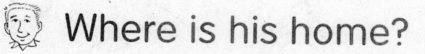 Where is his home?

 Let's find it.

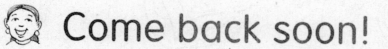 Come back soon!

Readers' Theater
© Harcourt • Grade 1 • Book 1

Is this pond the dog's home?

No, this is not the dog's home.

Where is his home?

Readers' Theater
© Harcourt • Grade 1 • Book 1

Is this the dog's home?

This is not the dog's home.

Let's go ask Mom now.

Yes! Let's ask Mom now!

 The dog is not lost.

This is the dog's home.

Oh! Thank you so much, Mom and Dad!

Make a Splash

Book 1-2

▶ **Read the sentences. Circle the sentence that tells about the picture.**

1. Peg fed the dog.

Peg lost the dog.

_____

2. This hen has ten pots.

This hen has ten eggs.

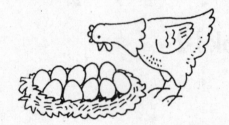

_____

3. The pen is on the desk.

The pen is on the dock.

_____

4. That jam is next to go.

That jet is next to go.

_____

5. Jeff is resting.

Jeff is calling.

School-Home Connection

Have your child read aloud all the sentences.
Ask your child to tell you the words that have
the short e sound, as in bed.

2

Practice Book
© Harcourt • Grade 1 • Book 2

Name _____

▶ **Read the Spelling Words. Then write each word in the group where it belongs.**

Words with e

_____   _____

_____   _____

_____   _____

_____   _____

_____   _____

_____

Words without e

_____

_____

_____

_____

Spelling Words

set

sent

ten

tell

let

get

all

call

make

of

🚌 **School–Home Connection**

Have your child read each Spelling Word
aloud. Talk about how the words are alike and
how they are different. Start by comparing the
words *set* and *sent*.

3

Practice Book
© Harcourt • Grade 1 • Book 2

► **Circle the word that completes each sentence. Then write the word.**

hen   hot

_____

- - - - - - - - - - - -

1. The _____ can peck.

pot   pet

_____

- - - - - - - - - - - -

2. She has a _____.

nod   nest

_____

- - - - - - - - - - - -

3. Jess sees a _____.

end   egg

_____

- - - - - - - - - - - -

4. Ken eats an _____.

bits   belts

_____

- - - - - - - - - - - -

5. The _____ will be on them.

Practice Book

▶ **Write a word from the box to complete each sentence.**

day	eat	first	said	time	was

1. "You can kick, Tess," he _____.

2. "I will kick _____."

3. It _____ a good kick.

4. Now it's _____ for Tess to kick.

5. It's the best kick of the _____!

Practice Book
© Harcourt • Grade 1 • Book 2

Name _____

▶ **Read about the animals. Complete the sentences. Tell how the animals are the same.**

The dog is big.
It is a pet.
It eats fast.

The hen is little.
It is a pet, too.
It pecks to eat.

_____
_ _

1. The hen and the dog _____.

_____
_ _

2. They _____ food.

▶ **Now complete these sentences. Tell how the animals are different.**

_____   _____
_ _ _ _ _ _ _ _ _ _ _ _ _ _ _   _ _ _ _ _ _ _ _ _ _ _ _ _ _

3. The dog is _____. It eats _____.

_____   _____
_ _ _ _ _ _ _ _ _ _ _ _ _ _ _   _ _ _ _ _ _ _ _ _ _ _ _ _ _

4. The hen is _____. It _____ to eat.

🚌 **School–Home Connection**

Ask your child to think of other ways the
animals are alike and different.

6

▶ **Write the word that completes each sentence.**

_____

1. He is in a _____ van.

back   black

_____

2. She likes _____.

plants   pants

_____

3. Meg _____ to pack.

plans   pans

_____

4. The land is _____.

fat   flat

_____

5. They _____ for him.

cap   clap

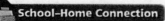 **School–Home Connection**

Have your child read the words and sentences
aloud to you. Talk about how the words in
each word pair are the same and different.

Practice Book
© Harcourt • Grade 1 • Book 2

Name _____

▶ **Look at the picture. Write exclamations to go with the picture.**

1. _____

_____

_____

2. _____

_____

_____

3. _____

_____

_____

4. _____

8

▶ **Circle the sentence that tells about each picture.**

1. The dog gets a bath.
   The dog gets a bat.

2. Dad and Mom met Beth.
   They met on the path.

3. The dog sits with a cat.
   The dog thinks that is a bat.

4. Mr. Glen is tenth.
   Mr. Glen is thin.

5. Jill sits with the dolls.
   Jill wants the fifth doll.

6. I thank the vet for her help.
   The pet thanks the vet.

School–Home Connection

Point to the words *bath* and *bat*. Talk about
how the words are alike and different.

9

▶ **Read the Spelling Words. Then write each word in the group where it belongs.**

Words with <u>th</u>

_____   _____

- - - - - - - - - - - - - - - -   - - - - - - - - - - - - - - - -

_____   _____

_____   _____

- - - - - - - - - - - - - - - -   - - - - - - - - - - - - - - - -

_____   _____

_____   _____

- - - - - - - - - - - - - - - -   - - - - - - - - - - - - - - - -

_____   _____

Words without <u>th</u>

_____   _____

- - - - - - - - - - - - - - - -   - - - - - - - - - - - - - - - -

_____   _____

_____   _____

- - - - - - - - - - - - - - - -   - - - - - - - - - - - - - - - -

_____   _____

Spelling Words

then

them

this

that

path

with

ten

get

said

was

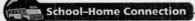
School–Home Connection

Have your child read each Spelling Word aloud.
Then take turns saying the words to each other
and writing them.

10

▶ **Look at each picture. Write a word
from the box to complete each sentence.**

sixth	thin	path	that	Beth

_____

1. _____ waters the plants.

_____

2. Ken is _____ in line.

_____

3. The cat is not too _____.

_____

4. I like _____ fish.

_____

5. Dot is on the _____.

School–Home Connection

Have your child read each completed sentence
aloud. Together, think of other words that
begin or end with *th*.

11

▶ **Write a word from the box to complete each sentence.**

don't	her	line	Mr.
new	says	water	

1. Meg picks up _____ things.

2. Todd _____ he will help.

3. Cliff will _____ the plants.

4. I _____ want to get wet.

5. Tom gets a _____ cloth.

6. _____ Glenn is glad to help.

Practice Book
© Harcourt • Grade 1 • Book 2

► **Read about Tim's dog. Write three details that tell about the dog.**

Tim has a dog. His dog is called Meg. She is a black dog. She is a little fat. The dog is so soft. Tim is glad he has Meg for a pet.

1. _____

_____

_____

2. _____

_____

_____

3. _____

_____

_____

13

▶ **Circle the word that completes each sentence. Then write the word.**

snack   stack

1. Jed fed his pet a _____.

skill   spill

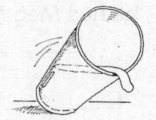

2. The milk will _____.

smells   spells

3. The ham _____ good.

slick   stick

4. The dog gets the _____.

slim   swim

5. Todd and Beth can _____.

School-Home Connection

Talk about the pictures. Say each sentence with
the incorrect word. Have your child read the
sentence correctly.

Practice Book
© Harcourt • Grade 1 • Book 2

▶ **Look at the picture. Write two sentences to go with the picture. Use nouns that name places and people.**

1. _____

_____

_____

2. _____

_____

_____

School–Home Connection

Have your child name people and places as
you write them down. Then read the list to
your child and ask him or her to say a sentence
using each name.

15

▶ **Write a word from the box to complete each sentence.**

jump	but	tuck	fun	dust	must

_____

1. Glen and Russ have _____ acting like frogs.

_____

2. "First, we _____ sit like this."

_____

3. "Then we _____ up and down."

_____

4. They kick up a lot of _____.

_____

5. Russ can't hop fast, _____ Glenn can.

 **School–Home Connection**

Ask your child to read aloud the completed sentences. Have him or her point to words that have the short u sound, as in hut.

16

Name _____

▶ **Read the Spelling Words. Then write each word in the group where it belongs.**

Words with u

_____   _____

- - - - - - - - - - - - -   - - - - - - - - - - - - -

_____   _____

- - - - - - - - - - - - -   - - - - - - - - - - - - -

_____   _____

- - - - - - - - - - - - -   - - - - - - - - - - - - -

Words without u

_____   _____

- - - - - - - - - - - - -   - - - - - - - - - - - - -

_____   _____

- - - - - - - - - - - - -   - - - - - - - - - - - - -

Spelling Words

us
bus
must
cut
cub
club
with
then
don't
says

School–Home Connection

Have your child read each Spelling Word
aloud. Then have your child identify the words
with the short *u* sound.

Practice Book
© Harcourt • Grade 1 • Book 2

▶ **Cross out the word that is wrong.**
Write the correct word.

1. This pig is in the mad.

_____

- - - - - - - - - - - - - - - -

_____

2. A beg is on her hand.

_____

- - - - - - - - - - - - - - - -

_____

3. A net is good to eat.

_____

- - - - - - - - - - - - - - - -

_____

4. He fills the jog.

_____

- - - - - - - - - - - - - - - -

_____

5. She sits on a stamp.

_____

- - - - - - - - - - - - - - - -

_____

6. The deck swims in the pond.

_____

- - - - - - - - - - - - - - - -

_____

School–Home Connection

Ask your child to read each sentence with the incorrect word and then reread it with the correct word.

18

▶ **Write a word from the box to complete each sentence.**

be	does	food	grow	live	many

1. They _____ next to a pond.

2. Plants _____ tall next to the water.

3. There are _____ bugs that like the pond.

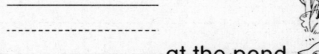

4. Ducks come there to look for _____.

5. Beth likes to _____ at the pond.

19

▶ **Read about the plant. Write three details that tell about this plant.**

I have a plant. It is in a black pot. This plant has a tall stem. There are two pink buds at the top. The buds are soft, and they smell good, too.

_____

1. _____

_____

2. _____

_____

3. _____

_____

School–Home Connection

Ask your child to think of a favorite game or toy. Have him or her tell details about it that make it a favorite.

20

▶ **Write r as the second letter in each word to make a new word. Then use the new words to complete the sentences.**

tuck	+ r	
cab	+ r	
tip	+ r	
fog	+ r	

_____ _____

1. The _____ and the _____ pack some bags.

_____ _____

2. They will go on a _____ in a _____.

School–Home Connection

With your child, think of words that begin with the letters *br, dr, gr,* and *tr.* Have your child write the first two letters of each word you say.

21

▶ **Circle the nouns. Then write four sentences. Use a noun from the box in each sentence.**

dig	dog	fox
hand	has	map
raft	sled	soft

1. _____

2. _____

3. _____

4. _____

Practice Book
© Harcourt • Grade 1 • Book 2

▶ **Circle the sentence that tells about each picture.**

1.

   Frank bangs the drums.

   Frank bags the drums.

2.

   This man sings a song.

   This man is a king.

3.

   Beth rings the bell.

   Beth brings the bell.

4.

   The bug hangs on a plant.

   The bug flings the plant.

5.

   Brent likes to swim.

   Brent likes to swing.

School-Home Connection

Write the words *bag* and *bang*. Have your child
read the words aloud. Talk about how each
word sounds and how it is spelled.

23

Name _____

▶ **Read the Spelling Words. Then write each word in the group where it belongs.**

Words with <u>ng</u>

_____   _____

_____   _____

_____   _____

_____   _____

_____   _____

Words without <u>ng</u>

_____   _____

_____   _____

_____   _____

School–Home Connection

Write the Spelling Words *long* and *sing*. Have your child change one letter in each word to make other Spelling Words (*song* and *ring*).

24

Name _____

▶ **Write a word from the box to complete each sentence.**

| long | brings | swung | ring | sang | wings |

_____

1. Bess has a _____ on her hand.

_____

2. Frank _____ at the ball.

_____

3. Some bugs have _____.

_____

4. This crab has _____ legs.

_____

5. Mom _____ me food to eat.

 School-Home Connection

Have your child read each completed sentence aloud. Together, think of other words that end with *ng*.

Practice Book
© Harcourt • Grade 1 • Book 2

Name _____

▶ **Write a word from the box to complete each sentence.**

arms	every	feet	head
school	use	way	your

1. Frank sings at _____ with his class.

2. Mr. Ling says, "Look this _____."

3. Then Mr. Ling says, "Clap _____ hands."

4. Frank swings his _____, too.

5. Frank will _____ the drums.

6. Frank taps his _____.

School–Home Connection

Ask your child to point to the words *every* and *head*. Have him or her use the words to write sentences.

26

Practice Book
© Harcourt • Grade 1 • Book 2

▶ **Read the story. Finish the sentences.**

It was a hot day. Glenn wanted to swim. "Mom, will you go with me so I can swim?" Glenn asked.

"I can't, Glenn. I am fixing the sink now," said Mom.

Glenn asked his dad, "Will you swim with me?"

"I can't," said Dad. "I am helping your mom."

Then Glenn's pal Matt called. "It's so hot!" said Matt. "Do you want to go with my dad and me to swim?"

"Yes, I do!" said Glenn. "Thank you!"

_____

I. Glenn wanted to _____.

_____

_____
----

2. First, _____ said no. Dad did, too.

_____

3. Glenn went to swim with

_____

_____

School–Home Connection

Have your child read the story aloud. Ask your
child why Glenn wanted to swim. (because it was
a hot day) Then ask what happened at the end.

Name _____

▶ **Write the contraction for the two words. Then read the sentence.**

We   will

_____

----

1. _____ get a snack to eat.

you   will

_____

----

2. I think _____ like this food.

He   will

_____

----

3. _____ make some ham for us.

she   will

_____

----

4. I think _____ have water to drink.

I   will

_____

----

5. _____ have some water, too.

School–Home Connection

Say sentences using the contractions *I'll*, *they'll*, and *we'll*. Ask your child to say each sentence again, but with the two words that make up each contraction.

Practice Book
© Harcourt • Grade 1 • Book 2

Name _____

▶ **Look around the room. What do you see? Write sentences that tell how many you see of some things.**

_____

1. _____

_____

_____

2. _____

_____

_____

3. _____

_____

_____

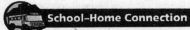

School–Home Connection

Play a game with your child. Name something that you have in your home or family. Have your child say a sentence that tells how many you have.

Practice Book

© Harcourt • Grade 1 • Book 2

▶ **Write the word that completes the sentence.**

trunk   thorn   tore
_____

----

1. A _____ cut my leg.

fork   flock   corn
_____

----

2. The _____ fell on the mat.

fort   forest   frog
_____

----

3. The frog lives in the _____ .

more   well   wore
_____

----

4. Sam _____ a jacket in the cold.

stop   sort   store
_____

----

5. He gets food at the _____ .

School–Home Connection

Have your child read each word and sentence
aloud. Talk about how the choices for each
item are alike and how they are different.

30

Practice Book
© Harcourt • Grade 1 • Book 2

▶ **Read the Spelling Words. Then write each word in the group where it belongs.**

Words with <u>or</u>

_____   _____

------------------------   ------------------------

_____   _____

_____   _____

------------------------   ------------------------

_____   _____

Words without <u>or</u>

_____   _____

------------------------   ------------------------

_____   _____

_____   _____

------------------------   ------------------------

Spelling Words

or
for
form
more
store
sort
long
bring
your
head

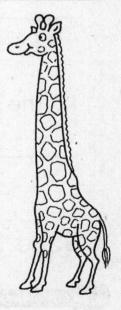

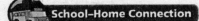
School–Home Connection

Play a version of *I Spy* with your child using the Spelling Word list. Say, for example, "I Spy words with *f*." Have your child write the words.

31

▶ **Look at each picture. Write a word from the box to complete each sentence.**

more	storm	snores	corn	snorts	shore

1. The pig eats lots of _____.

2. The pig _____ as he naps.

3. The _____ will stop soon.

4. The pig wants _____ food.

5. He _____ at us.

School–Home Connection

Have your child read each word in the box aloud. Together, think of other words spelled with *or* or *ore* that have the /ôr/ sound.

Practice Book
© Harcourt • Grade 1 • Book 2

▶ **Write a word from the box to complete each sentence.**

animals	cold	fish	from
their	under	very	

1. I have pet _____.

2. One swims _____ a big fish.

3. My water is _____. The water for my fish is not cold.

4. My pals have _____, too.

5. Doris has a _____ plump rabbit.

6. The twins run with _____ dog.

School–Home Connection

Have your child write a sentence using the word *from*. Encourage him or her to use the other words in sentences, too.

33

Name _____

▶ **Look at the pictures and read the sentences. Complete the sentence that follows by telling how the things are alike.**

Helen has socks.

They are on her feet.

Her socks are red.

Helen has mittens, too.

They are on her hands.

They are black.

_____

1. The socks and mittens belong to _____.

_____

_____

▶ **Now tell how the things are different.**

_____

2. The socks _____.

_____

3. The mittens _____.

School-Home Connection
Together, think of items of clothing that your child wears. Talk about how the items are alike and how they are different.

 34

Name _____

▶ **Say each word and picture name together to make a new word. Write the new word. Then use the words to complete the sentences.**

 + hill =	_____
sand + ☐ =	_____
👦 ⬅ + pack =	_____

_____

1. Grant went to dig in the _____.

_____

2. An _____ was hidden in the grass.

_____

3. Ants got into his _____.

School–Home Connection

Have your child read the words and sentences aloud. Together, think of other words that can be put together to make new words.

Practice Book
© Harcourt • Grade 1 • Book 2

▶ **Write a letter to a friend. Tell about
yourself and your family. Write special
names and titles correctly.**

_____

- -

Dear _____,

_____

- -

_____

- -

_____

- -

_____

- -

_____

Your pal,

_____

- -

_____

School–Home Connection

Write a list with your child of special names
and titles of people you know. Read them
together. Point out the capital letters.

▶ **Write the word that completes the sentence.**

_____
- -

1. I made eggs. They are on a _____ .

dish   dash

_____
- - - - - - - - - - - - - - - - - - -

2. I can make _____ , too.

fish   short

_____
- - - - - - - - - - - - - - - - - - - -

3. I _____ I could make apple crisp.

shrug   wish

_____
- -

4. I will _____ for apples.

ship   shop

_____
- -

5. I will get a _____ , too.

radish   finish

School–Home Connection

Have your child read each completed sentence
aloud. Ask your child what is the same about
all the word choices. (They all have the *sh*
sound.)

37

Practice Book
© Harcourt • Grade 1 • Book 2

▶ **Read the Spelling Words. Then write each word in the group where it belongs.**

Words with <u>sh</u>

_____   _____

_____   _____

_____   _____

_____   _____

Words without <u>sh</u>

_____   _____

_____   _____

_____   _____

🚌 **School–Home Connection**

Ask your child to write all the Spelling Words
with *o* on a sheet of paper. Encourage your
child to continue this activity with *u*, *i*, and *e*.

► **Write the word from the box that completes the sentence.**

cash	finished	shop
shelf	rush	

_____

1. We will _____ at the mall.

_____

2. I have _____ to get a doll.

_____

3. I see dolls on a _____.

_____

4. I _____ to get a doll.

_____

5. We have _____.

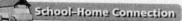
School-Home Connection

Have your child read each completed sentence
aloud. Together, think of other words with the
sh sound, as in *shop* and *rush*.

39

▶ **Write a word from the box to complete the sentence.**

happy	came	could	gold
made	night	saw	were

1. The king gave Doris a _____ ring.

2. The gift made her very _____.

3. Frog _____ to look at her ring.

4. He asked if he _____ hold it.

5. The ring was _____ just for Doris.

School–Home Connection

Ask your child to read aloud the words in the
box and the completed sentences. Then invite
your child to create sentences to continue the
story, using *night, saw,* and *were.*

Practice Book
© Harcourt • Grade 1 • Book 2

Name _____

▶ **Read each story beginning. Circle the picture that shows the setting.**

1. This morning, I helped Mom pick corn.

"That bucket is filled with corn now," Mom said.

"Let's go get some eggs from the hens."

"Then can we go to see the pigs?" I asked.

"Yes, we will go to see the pigs, too," Mom said.

2. It was time for bed.

"Is there a blanket I can have?" Ellen asked Bess.

"My blanket is not soft."

"I will give you my blanket," Bess said. "Will you let me go on the top bunk?"

School–Home Connection

Talk about a story that you and your child
know. Ask your child to tell you where and
when the story takes place.

41

Name _____

▶ **Write the words where they belong in the puzzle.**

| crab | skunk | blanket | sled | block |

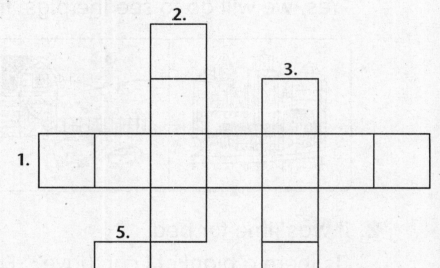

1.

2.

3.

4.

5.

School–Home Connection

Write the words *snack*, *brush*, and *flip*. Say a
clue for each, not in order, and have your child
point to the correct word.

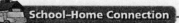

▶ **Circle each sentence that is written correctly.**

1. Hank lives on York Way.

2. Beth lives by flag cliff.

3. Trish lives next to the Red Mitten Store.

4. Todd lives by sunset shore.

5. Dennis and Jen live on top of Rust Hill.

▶ **Now write the other sentences correctly.**

6. _____

_____

_____

7. _____

_____

_____

School-Home Connection

With your child, draw a map of your neighborhood. Write the names of special places such as stores, schools, and churches. Use capital letters.

43

Cut-Out/ Fold-Up Books

Meg's Bad Day

"Yes, I have time, Meg," said Ted.

— Fold — — Fold —

8   "You fixed my bad day!" said Meg.

"Ted!" said Meg.
"Help me fix the well!"

6

45

4

"Ted," said Meg. "All day we
see this mess. Can you fix it?"

2

"Ted!" called Meg. "Will you
fix the bed? A leg fell off."

— Fold —

— Fold —

5

"You bet!" Ted said to Meg.

7

"Here I come, Meg!" said Ted.

46

Where Is Seth?

1

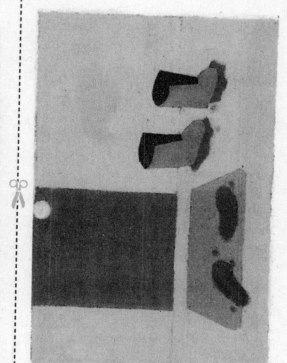

Is he at home?

3

"Here I am, Mom!" says Seth.

8

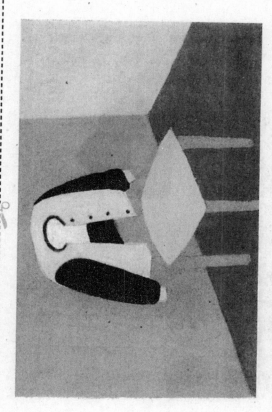

"I don't see Seth," Mom says.

6

47

4

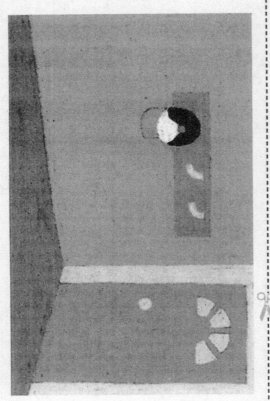

He left his new cap on a peg.

2

Mom looks for Seth.

Fold

Fold

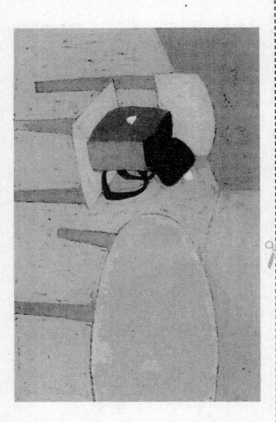

He set his bag down here.

5

Did Seth eat here?

Mom thinks so.

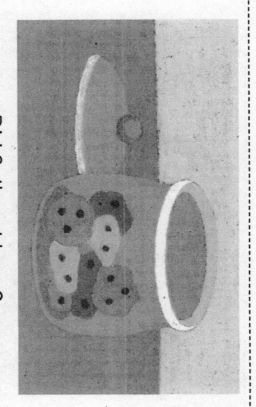

7

We Can Find It

1

"I see many things up here," says Scott. "Here is the pig."

3

---Fold---

"Thanks! Now we all have what we want."

8

"Where can my cat be?" says Scott.
"We can all hunt for it," says Tim.

6

---Fold---

49

© Harcourt • Grade 1 • Book 2 • Cut-Out/Fold-Up Book

"Where can my pig be?" asks Bess.

2 "Scott, do you see my pig?"

4 "I want my food," says Tim.
"Where can my food be?"

Fold

"What does it look like?" Tim asks.
"I see the cat, Scott," says Bess. 7

"I will get it for you," says Scott.
He gives the food to Tim. 5

Practice Book
© Harcourt • Grade 1 • Book 2 • Cut-Out/Fold-Up Book

Frog Songs

1

Fred uses his arms and feet to hop.

He has lots of bugs to eat.

3

Fold

Fold

Now it is time to go back home.

8

This is the way they like to sing.

6

51

4

Fred is a frog at Moss Pond.

He likes to hop on every rock.

Fred sings songs at school.

This is the way Fred uses his arms.

The song ends with a bang!

7

Every day they make up songs.

5

52

Fold

Fold

One More Thing

"Mom, can I have just one more?"

Fold

Fold

I like kisses from Mom very much!

8

"This is the last one.
Then you'll go to bed.

6

53

2

This snack is from Mom.
I like this snack very much.

✂

4

"Here's one more for you.
Then it will be time for bed."

— Fold —

"Thank you! I want just one
more thing from you, Mom."

✂

7

— Fold —

"I see one more, Mom.
Can I have one more from here?"

5

Practice Book
© Harcourt • Grade 1 • Book 2 • Cut-Out/Fold-Up Book

Brad Shops for Fish

Fold

Fold

They picked out a fish tank. They got many things for their fish.

Brad made a home for his fish.

How many fish do you see?

8

Dad got fish food from the shelf. Brad looked at the fish. He saw some that were gold and black.

6

2

Brad and his dad came to
the fish shop.

4

Some rocks, shells, and a ship
could look grand.

Fold

7

Brad picked his fish. They were
two very big fish. Now he and
his dad could go home.

5

They got plants to make
their fish happy.

Fold

The Frog and the Ox

Characters

Mom Frog **Dad Frog** **Granddad** **Jack** **Jill**

 Ribbit, ribbit. Ribbit, ribbit.

 It's a hot day at the pond!

 Yes! I am happy I am in the cold water.

 Here come some animals looking for a drink.

 I see an ox and two cubs.

 That ox is very big.

  Very, very big!

57

I wish I were that big.

No frog could be that big.

I am a very big frog.

You *are* big, but frogs don't get as big as an ox.

You could not live like a frog if you were that big.

Just think of the splash if an ox jumped into the water!

Still, I wish I were that big.

58

What are you doing?

  He has puffed himself
up to make himself look big.

 Mom says, "If you want to grow,
you must eat a lot of bugs."

 He is still puffed up.

 Stop now! You are still
smaller than the ox.

 You must use your head.
You can't be as big as an ox..

59

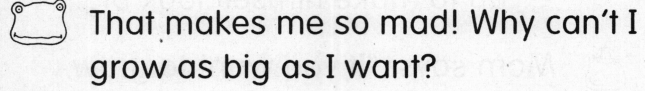 That makes me so mad! Why can't I grow as big as I want?

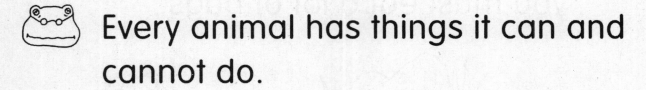 Every animal has things it can and cannot do.

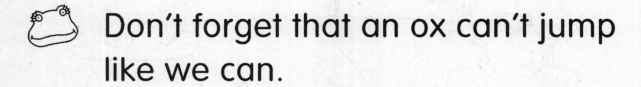 Don't forget that an ox can't jump like we can.

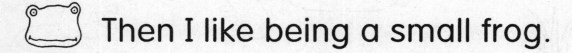 Then I like being a small frog.

 Me, too!

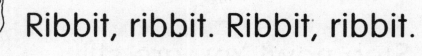 Ribbit, ribbit. Ribbit, ribbit.

Name _____

▶ **Read about Pam's cat. Write three details that tell about the cat.**

Pam has a cat. Her cat is called Simba. He naps in the sun. He sits in Pam's lap. Pam likes to hold Simba.

_____

1. _____

_____

_____

_____

2. _____

_____

_____

_____

3. _____

_____

_____

_____

School–Home Connection
Ask your child to think of their favorite kind of animal. Have him or her tell details about it.

61

Practice Book
© Harcourt • Grade 1 • Book 2

Name _____

▶ **Read the name of each group.**
Then circle all the things that belong
in that group.

1. Things that are small

_____

2. Things that talk

_____

3. Animals

_____

4. Things you can eat

 Try This

Think of other things that can go in each group.
Draw pictures.

School-Home Connection
Together, think of other group names. Then
think of things that can go in each group.

 62

Name _____

▶ **Read about the animals. Complete the
sentence. Tell how the animals are the same.**

The deer lives in the forest.
It is tall.
It has a long neck.

The cub lives in the forest, too.
It is little.
It has a short neck.

_____

1. The deer and the cub live _____

_____

_____.

▶ **Now tell how the animals are different.**

_____

2. The deer has a _____ neck.

_____

3. The cub has a _____ neck.

School–Home Connection

Ask your child to name other ways the animals
are alike and different.

63

Your Best Game

Book 1-3

Phonics:
Digraph /ch/*ch*,
Trigraph /ch/*tch*

Lesson 13

▶ **Circle the word that completes each sentence. Then write the word.**

branch   **brush**   **brand**

_____

1. The cat sits on a _____.

chunk   **crush**   **crutch**

_____

2. Chad must use a _____.

best   **bent**   **bench**

_____

3. We sit on the _____ to eat.

catch   **chest**   **chunk**

_____

4. My doll is in the _____.

desk   **ditch**   **dish**

_____

5. The dog is in the _____.

 **School–Home Connection**
Have your child read the sentences aloud.
Together, think of more words with *ch* or *tch*.

 2

Practice Book
© Harcourt • Grade 1 • Book 3

Name _____

Digraph /ch/ch,
Trigraph /ch/tch
Lesson 13

▶ **Read the Spelling Words. Then write each word in the group where it belongs.**

Words with <u>ch</u>

_____   _____

- - - - - - - - - - - - - -   - - - - - - - - - - - - - -

_____   _____

_____   _____

- - - - - - - - - - - - - -   - - - - - - - - - - - - - -

_____   _____

- - - - - - - - - - - - - -   - - - - - - - - - - - - - -

_____   _____

Words without <u>ch</u>

_____   _____

- - - - - - - - - - - - - -   - - - - - - - - - - - - - -

_____   _____

- - - - - - - - - - - - - -   - - - - - - - - - - - - - -

_____   _____

Spelling Words

chip
chin
inch
such
catch
match
wish
shop
saw
were

School–Home Connection

Have your child read each Spelling Word aloud. Ask him or her to circle the two Spelling Words that have a *t*. (*catch, match*)

3

Practice Book
© Harcourt • Grade 1 • Book 3

Name _____

Phonics:
Digraph /ch/*ch,*
Trigraph /ch/*tch*

Lesson 13

▶ **Circle the sentence that tells about each picture.**

1. Mitch is the chess champ.

Mitch chomps his lunch.

2. Rich will sketch the branch.

Rich will fetch the stick.

3. Some chicks will hatch soon.

The children check the test.

4. Chad does not like punch.

Chad does not like to pitch.

5. Ellen can stitch a patch.

Ellen can sketch an ostrich.

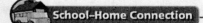
School–Home Connection

Have your child read each sentence aloud.
Ask him or her to draw a picture for a sentence
that is not circled.

4

Practice Book
© Harcourt • Grade 1 • Book 2

▶ **Write a word from the box to complete each sentence.**

air	fly	friends	grew
need	play	rain	watch

_____
- - - - - - - - - - - - - - - -

1. I see a robin _____ in the air.

_____
- - - - - - - - - - - - - - - -

2. My _____ see it, too.

_____
- - - - - - - - - - - - - - - -

3. Does it want to _____ with us?

_____
- - - - - - - - - - - - - - - -

4. We _____ the robin make a nest.

_____
- - - - - - - - - - - - - - - -

5. The robin will _____ to rest.

🚌 **School–Home Connection**

Write each word from the box on a separate slip of paper. Place the words face down. Have your child pick a word, read it aloud, and then use it in a sentence.

5

► **Think about what happens in each picture. Then answer each question.**

1. What happens to the plant first?

_____

- -

_____

_____

2. What does the plant get next?

_____

- -

_____

_____

3. What happens last?

_____

- -

_____

_____

School–Home Connection

Together, talk about how animals and plants
grow. Talk about the order in which the events
happen.

Practice Book
© Harcourt • Grade 1 • Book 3

► **Add es to the words in the box.**
Then write the correct word in each
sentence.

toss	sketch	branch	buzz	fix	dish

_____
- -

1. Mr. Sanchez _____ my backpack.

_____
- -

2. Liz _____ the ball.

_____
- -

3. Mitch helps with the _____.

_____
- -

4. Meg _____ a finch.

_____
- -

5. A storm made _____ fall.

7

▶ **Write sentences about your favorite two months. Tell what you like to do during each month. Write the sentences correctly.**

January	February	March	April
May	June	July	August
September	October	November	December

1. _____
   _____
   _____
   _____

2. _____
   _____
   _____

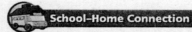

School–Home Connection

Ask your child what the names of the months
all have in common when you write them.
(They all start with a capital letter.) Talk about
what you like best about different months.

▶ **Circle the word that completes each sentence. Then write the word.**

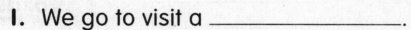

from   farm   form

_____

----

1. We go to visit a _____ .

_____

chat   cart   chart

_____

----

2. There is an animal _____ on a wall.

_____

band   barn   born

_____

----

3. Some animals are in the _____ .

_____

hard   had   here

_____

----

4. Some of us help with _____ chores.

_____

starch   stork   start

_____

5. We _____ to get in the bus to go home.

Practice Book
© Harcourt • Grade 1 • Book 3

Name _____

▶ **Read the Spelling Words. Then write each word in the group where it belongs.**

Words with <u>ar</u>

_____   _____

_____   _____

_____   _____

_____   _____

_____   _____

_____   _____

Words without <u>ar</u>

_____   _____

_____   _____

_____   _____

School–Home Connection

Have your child read each Spelling Word aloud. Write the word *art* and have your child add one letter to make the word *part*. Repeat with *arm* and *farm*.

10

Practice Book
© Harcourt • Grade 1 • Book 3

Name _____

▶ **Cross out the word that is wrong.**
Write the correct word.

1. We are at a form.

_____

- - - - - - - - - - - - - - - - - - - -

_____

2. We went into the born.

_____

- - - - - - - - - - - - - - - - - - - -

_____

3. Mr. Brent got a cord.

_____

- - - - - - - - - - - - - - - - - - - -

_____

4. We went to the pork.

_____

- - - - - - - - - - - - - - - - - - - -

_____

5. I have a cast on
my am.

_____

- - - - - - - - - - - - - - - - - - - -

_____

6. Dad will use the cat
to shop.

_____

- - - - - - - - - - - - - - - - - - - -

_____

School–Home Connection

Say a sentence with one incorrect word. Ask
your child to say the sentence correctly.

11

▶ **Write the word from the box that completes the sentence.**

again	feel	house	know
loud	Mrs.	put	say

_____
- - - - - - - - - - - - - - - - - -
1. _____ Marsh asked Scarlet to help.

_____

_____
- - - - - - - - - - - - - - - - - - - -
2. Scarlet and the dog went out of the _____.

_____

_____
- - - - - - - - - - - - - - - - - - - -
3. Scarlet was happy to play with the dog _____.

_____

_____
- - - - - - - - - - - - - - - - - -
4. "I _____ he wants to run in the yard,"
Scarlet said.

_____

_____
- - - - - - - - - - - - - - - - -
5. The dog had a _____ bark.

 **School–Home Connection**

Have your child find the words *feel*, *say*, and
put in the box. Ask him or her to use them in
sentences.

12

Name _____

▶ **Circle the picture that shows who is telling each story. Then circle the sentence that tells why the author wrote it.**

Helping Lost Pets by Liz Smith

My dog, Max, has a tag. The tag tells where his home is. It tells who to call if Max is lost. If you find a lost pet, look at its tag.

1.

2. Liz Smith wants us to know how to help lost pets.

   Liz Smith wants us to get a dog.

Dog Fun! by Martin Hill

Bark! Sniff! Run and jump! Lick! Wag!
Thump, thump, thump! Let's go to the park!
Let's have fun! I'll catch the ball. I'll run and run!

3.

4. The author wants us to have fun reading this.

   The author wants us to pet a dog.

School–Home Connection
Talk about a story that you and your child know. Discuss why the author might have written the story.

13

Name _____

► **Write a word from the box to complete each sentence.**

banged	started	checks
looked	acting	thinks

_____

1. Tom was _____ in the play.

_____

2. He _____ to say his part.

_____

3. Helen _____ the drums.

_____

4. Mrs. Hill _____ the clock.

_____

5. She _____ we will finish the play soon.

School–Home Connection

Have your child read each completed sentence aloud. Together, practice adding -s, -ed, and -ing to other words and using the new words in sentences.

14

Practice Book
© Harcourt • Grade 1 • Book 3

Name _____

▶ **Write three sentences about your favorite holidays. Write the names of the holidays correctly.**

1. _____

_____

_____

_____

2. _____

_____

_____

_____

3. _____

_____

_____

School–Home Connection

Make a list of holidays that your family celebrates. Talk about each holiday. Encourage your child to draw and label a picture for his or her favorite holiday.

15

Practice Book
© Harcourt • Grade 1 • Book 3

▶ **Read the sentences. Circle the sentence that tells about the picture.**

1.

   Cliff has a quilt on his bed.

   Cliff has a quack on his bed.

2.

   "I will quit pecking corn."

   "When will my eggs hatch?"

3.

   "Is this is a quick car?"

   "Which ball do you want?"

4.

   The ducks quack all day.

   The ducks quit all day.

5.

   Ted quacks at the ball.

   Ted whacks the ball.

School–Home Connection

Point to the words *quack* and *whacks*. Talk about how the words are alike and different.

16

Name _____

▶ **Read the Spelling Words. Then write each word in the group where it belongs.**

Words with <u>wh</u>

_____   _____
- - - - - - - - - - - - - -   - - - - - - - - - - - - - -
_____   _____

_____
- - - - - - - - - - - - - -

_____

Words with <u>qu</u>

_____   _____
- - - - - - - - - - - - - -   - - - - - - - - - - - - - -
_____   _____

_____
- - - - - - - - - - - - - -

_____

Spelling Words

quit

quick

quiz

whiz

which

when

arm

part

house

put

Other Words

_____   _____
- - - - - - - - - - - - - -   - - - - - - - - - - - - - -
_____   _____

_____   _____
- - - - - - - - - - - - - -   - - - - - - - - - - - - - -

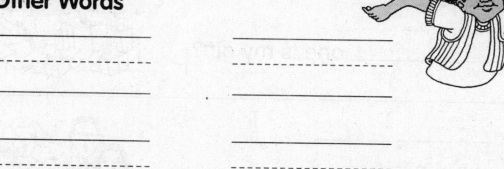

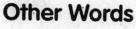 **School–Home Connection**

Ask your child to point to each Spelling Word
with an *i* and read it aloud. Then have him or
her read the other words aloud and name the
vowels used.

Practice Book
© Harcourt • Grade 1 • Book 3

▶ **Look at each picture. Write the word in the box that completes the sentence.**

Which	quick	quit	When	whip	Quinn

_____

----

1. Karl is so _____ !

_____

----

2. _____ has a shell.

_____

----

3. _____ can I go out?

_____

----

4. _____ one is my gift?

_____

----

5. He _____ singing.

School–Home Connection

Have your child read each completed sentence
aloud. Together, think of other words that
begin with *qu* and *wh*.

18

Practice Book
© Harcourt • Grade 1 • Book 3

▶ **Write a word from the box to complete each sentence.**

about	books	family	name
people	read	work	writing

_____
- - - - - - - - - - - - - - - - - - - -

1. Mark is _____ a list.

_____
- - - - - - - - - - - - - - - - - - - -

2. The _____ are on his desk.

_____
- - - - - - - - - - - - - - - - - - - -

3. Beth sits on the rug to _____.

_____
- - - - - - - - - - - - - - - - - - - -

4. Scarlet tells us _____ her pet.

_____
- - - - - - - - - - - - - - - - - - - -

5. Marvin prints his _____.

_____
- - - - - - - - - - - - - - - - - - - -

6. Chuck can _____ with Tess.

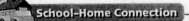

School–Home Connection

Have your child read *people* and *family*. Ask your child to name the people in your family.

19

▶ **Read each group of sentences. Write 1, 2, 3, or 4 in front of each sentence to tell the order in which the events happen.**

1. _____ A chick comes out of the egg.

   _____ The egg hatches.

   _____ The chick grows up to be a hen.

   _____ A hen sits on her egg.

2. _____ The corn plants grow tall.

   _____ It is time to sell the corn.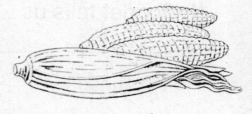

   _____ The corn is picked and put in buckets.

   _____ Corn is planted on a farm.

School–Home Connection
Talk about a favorite dish you and your child like to cook. Have your child tell the order in which steps are done to prepare the dish.

Practice Book
© Harcourt • Grade 1 • Book 3

Name _____

▶ **Write the word that completes the sentence.**

1. I _____ with Janet.

**skipped
skipping**

_____

2. They _____ the song.

**hummed
humming**

_____

3. She is _____ to sing.

**planned
planning**

_____

4. He _____ about
his big dog.

**bragged
bragging**

_____

5. Frank's bag _____.

**ripped
ripping**

School–Home Connection

Ask your child to write the word *skipped* and
then underline *skip*. Repeat for other words on
this page that end with *ed* or *ing*.

21

► **Complete the sentence, using <u>I</u> or <u>me</u>.**
Write the sentence correctly.

1. _____ like to swim

_____

- - - - - - - - - - - - - - - - - - - -

_____

2. my chicks swim with _____

_____

- - - - - - - - - - - - - - - - - - - -

_____

3. _____ can quack

_____

- - - - - - - - - - - - - - - - - - - -

_____

4. you can see _____

_____

- - - - - - - - - - - - - - - - - - - -

_____

5. _____ am a duck.

_____

- - - - - - - - - - - - - - - - - - - -

_____

School–Home Connection

Have your child write sentences about an
animal that might live in a zoo. Ask him or her
to write one sentence using *I* and one sentence
using *me*.

22

Name _____

▶ **Circle the sentence that tells about the picture.**

1. Her cat is on her shirt.
   The girl pets her cat's soft fur.

---

2. It turns in her lap and purrs.
   Her pet slurps the water.

---

3. She will read to her mom.
   She will read to herself.

---

4. A bird sits and chirps.
   This bird is not on a branch.

---

5. The girl sees the bird first.
   The bird makes its first nest.

---

6. The cat and bird are in the dirt.
   The bird flaps as the cat squirms.

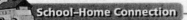

School–Home Connection

Point to the words *girl, her,* and *fur* in the
second sentence. Have your child read the
words aloud. Ask how the words are alike.

23

▶ **Read the Spelling Words. Then write each word in the group where it belongs.**

Words with r

_____   _____

_____   _____

_____   _____

_____   _____

_____   _____

_____   _____

_____

Spelling Words

her

fur

turn

bird

girl

first

quit

when

name

work

Words without r

_____   _____

_____   _____

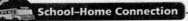
School–Home Connection

Have your child put a checkmark by the
Spelling Words with *ur* and a star by the
Spelling Words with *ir*. Then have him or her
circle the Spelling Word with *er*.

Practice Book
© Harcourt • Grade 1 • Book 3

▶ **Write a word from the box to complete each sentence.**

fur	perched	turn
first	curl	dirt

_____

----

1. He's the _____ to get into the raft.

_____

----

2. Now it is Mom and Dad's _____.

_____

----

3. A bird is _____ in a tree.

_____

----

4. This animal's _____ is wet.

_____

----

5. We see it digging in the _____.

School–Home Connection

Write the words *her*, *thirst*, and *sunburn*. Ask your child to read the words and use them in sentences.

25

▶ **Write a word from the box to complete each sentence.**

| always | by | Cow's | join |
| Please | nice | room | |

_____
- -
1. Bird _____ likes to visit his friends.

_____
- - - - - - - - - - - - - - - - - - - -
2. "Have a _____ time!" his mom said.

_____
- - - - - - - - - - - - - - - - - - - -
3. Bird went to _____ barn.

" _____
- - - - - - - - - - - - - - - - - - - -
4. _____ come in," his friend said.

_____
- - - - - - - - - - - - - - - - - - - -
5. "You can _____ the fun," Hen said.

School–Home Connection

Ask your child to find the words *room* and *by*
in the box. Then have him or her write the
words in sentences to add to the story above.

26

Practice Book
© Harcourt • Grade 1 • Book 3

▶ **Read the story. Look at the picture.**
Circle the sentence that tells the main
idea of the story.

1.   Hen went on a picnic with her friends. They had
sandwiches to eat. Duck and Skunk played catch
with a ball. Then they all had fun swimming in
the pond.

Animals have fun at a picnic.
The animals swim.

2.   Summer is here! The sun is up. It is a hot day.
Birds are singing. Children are in the park. Some
are running. Summer is fun!

It is a hot day.
We have fun in the summer.

3.   Dan bumped his leg. Now his leg hurts. Dan can
see a red spot on his leg. It's starting to swell. He
gets help from his mom.

Dan has hurt his leg.
Dan's mom is nice.

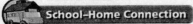

School–Home Connection

Read each story with your child. Together,
think of a good title for each one. Choose a
title that tells what the story is mainly about.

27

▶ **Look at the picture. Then write the word that completes the sentence.**

_____

1. The cat is _____
   than the pig.

| smaller |
| smallest |

_____

_____

2. The ostrich is the _____.

| taller |
| tallest |

_____

_____

3. The hen is the _____.

| shorter |
| shortest |

_____

_____

4. The dog's legs are _____
   than the hen's legs.

| longer |
| longest |

🪐 **Try This**

Add <u>er</u> and <u>est</u> to the word <u>fast</u>. Draw pictures of three animals. Use the words to label the pictures.

School-Home Connection

Have your child compare things in your home, using words that end in *er* and *est*.

28

▶ **Circle each sentence pair that is written correctly.**

1. Karl is at the pond. He sits on a bench.

2. Mark and Tom play. He are friends.

3. Beth fixes popcorn. He drinks milk, too.

4. There is a nest. It is on a branch.

▶ **Now write the other sentences. Write the pronouns correctly.**

5. _____

_____

_____

6. _____

_____

School–Home Connection

Say a sentence, using the name of a person,
animal, or thing. Have your child repeat the
sentence, using a pronoun in place of the name.

29

▶ **Circle the word that completes each sentence. Then write the word.**

candle   little   ripple

_____

- -

1. I have a _____ sister.

_____

purple   tickle   tattle

_____

- -

2. Mom lets me _____ her feet.

_____

kettle   gobble   giggle

_____

- -

3. It makes my sister _____ .

_____

rattle   riddle   gurgle

_____

- -

4. She likes to play with a _____ .

_____

bubble   fiddle   bottle

_____

- -

5. She drinks from a _____ .

School–Home Connection

Have your child read each completed sentence
aloud. Ask him or her to choose a word that
was not circled and to write a sentence with it.

30

Practice Book

© Harcourt • Grade 1 • Book 3

Name _____

▶ **Read the Spelling Words. Then write each word in the group where it belongs.**

Words with le

_____

- - - - - - - - - - - - - - - - - -

_____

- - - - - - - - - - - - - - - - - -

_____

_____

- - - - - - - - - - - - - - - - - -

_____

- - - - - - - - - - - - - - - - - -

_____

Words without le

_____

- - - - - - - - - - - - - - - - - -

_____

- - - - - - - - - - - - - - - - - -

_____

- - - - - - - - - - - - - - - - - -

_____

_____

- - - - - - - - - - - - - - - - - -

_____

- - - - - - - - - - - - - - - - - -

_____

- - - - - - - - - - - - - - - - - -

_____

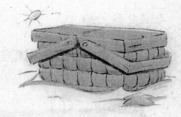

School–Home Connection

Write the words *hand*, *sing*, *wig*, and *lit*. Have your child read the words aloud. Then ask him or her to add letters to these words to make Spelling Words.

31

▶ **Write a word from the box to complete each sentence.**

giggle	puddle	ripples
ankles	middle	pebble

1. Jan saw a _____ of water. _____

2. She tossed a _____ into it.

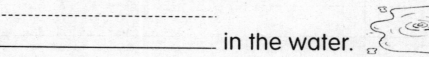

3. It landed in the _____ of the puddle.

4. It made _____ in the water.

5. Jan got her _____ wet.

Practice Book
© Harcourt • Grade 1 • Book 3

▶ **Write a word from the box to complete each sentence.**

buy	carry	money	other
paint	paper	would	

_____
- - - - - - - - - - - - - - - - - - - -

1. Pam has _____ to get what she needs.

_____
- - - - - - - - - - - - - - - - - - - -

2. She'll _____ brushes for her art.

_____
- - - - - - - - - - - - - - - - - - - -

3. She'll need blank _____, too.

_____
- - - - - - - - - - - - - - - - - - - -

4. Mom helps Pam _____ the bags.

_____
- - - - - - - - - - - - - - - - - - - -

5. Pam plans to _____ farm animals.

Practice Book
© Harcourt • Grade 1 • Book 3

▶ **Read the sentences. Then circle the best answer to the question.**

Turtles have hard shells. If you startle a turtle, it will go inside its shell. A pond turtle has flat feet. Its feet help it to dig in mud. Other turtles have flippers for swimming.

1. What is this about?

It is about shells.

It is about feet.

It is about turtles.

Many animals hatch from eggs. Birds and ducks hatch from eggs. Their eggs are kept in nests. Turtles hatch from eggs, too. Turtles dig pits in the sand. That's where their eggs are kept. Some insects and frogs hatch from eggs in water.

2. What is this about?

It is about birds.

It is about animals that hatch from eggs.

It is about animals that swim in the water.

School–Home Connection
Have your child read each story. Ask your child what details helped him or her to figure out the main idea of the story.

34

Practice Book
© Harcourt • Grade 1 • Book 3

Name _____

▶ **Add the endings _ed_ and _ing_ to each word. Remember to double the last letter.**

	ed	ing
1. jog	jogged	
2. nap		
3. zip		

▶ **Write a word from the chart to complete each sentence.**

4. Pig _____ to the camp.

5. Has he _____ up the tent?

6. Now he is _____ .

School–Home Connection

Write *drip*. Ask your child to rewrite the word
with the endings -*ed* and -*ing*. Remind him or
her to double the last letter in *drip*.

35

Practice Book
© Harcourt • Grade 1 • Book 3

▶ **Circle each sentence that is written correctly.**

1. Tom buckles its belt

2. Ella pets her turtle.

3. Ben and Mom pack their bags.

4. The bobcat licks yours fur.

5. Is this magnet yours?

▶ **Now write the other sentences correctly.**

6. _____
_____
_____

7. _____
_____
_____

School-Home Connection

Find objects in the house that belong to you,
your child, and other family members. Talk
about the objects using possessive pronouns
such as *my, your, our, his, her.*

▶ **Write the words where they belong in the puzzle.**

| coat | crow | road | snow | soap | throw |

1.

2.

3.

4.

5.

6.

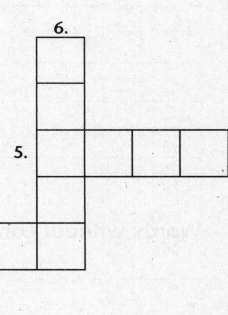

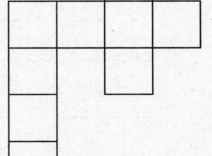

Practice Book
© Harcourt • Grade 1 • Book 3

▶ **Read the Spelling Words. Then write each word in the group where it belongs.**

Words with Long o

_____   _____

_____   _____

_____   _____

_____   _____

low
slow
grow
road
soap
boat
little
handle
carry
would

Words without Long o

_____   _____

_____   _____

_____   _____

School–Home Connection

Write, "I rode to the end of the road and then rowed across the river." Read the sentence aloud and have your child circle the Spelling Word. (*road*)

38

Practice Book
© Harcourt • Grade 1 • Book 3

Name _____

▶ **Circle the sentence that tells about each picture.**

1. Joan will row the boat.
   Joan will go across the road.

2. There's a fellow by the window.
   He rests his elbow on a pillow.

3. The crow follows the goat.
   The toad croaks at a minnow.

4. He has a boat on the coast.
   I wore my coat in the snow.

5. I soap up as I soak in the tub.
   I have a bath in a tugboat.

6. Quinn towed a boat on the pond.
   Quinn floated on the pond.

School-Home Connection
Have your child read each sentence aloud. Ask
him or her to choose a sentence that is not
circled and draw a picture for it.

39

▶ **Write a word from the box to complete each sentence.**

mouse	our	over
pretty	surprise	three

1. Can Ann come _____ to play?

2. Yes, Ann can come to _____ house.

3. Ann thinks my dolls are _____.

4. I have _____ dolls on my bed.

5. I have a stuffed _____, too.

School–Home Connection

Ask your child to read aloud the word *surprise*
from the box. Ask your child to describe a
surprise that he or she has enjoyed.

Practice Book
© Harcourt • Grade 1 • Book 3

Name _____

▶ **Read each story. Then circle the sentence that tells why the author wrote the story.**

Plants

by Brent Hall

All plants need water to live. Some plants need only a little water. Other plants need a lot. Plants need sun, too. Most potted plants are kept next to a window.

1. Brent Hall wants us to know about water.

   Brent Hall wants us to know what plants need.

_____

Helen's Dog

by Fran Miller

Helen was watering her plants. She spilled some water. There was a puddle at her feet. She didn't have a cloth or a mop. She didn't know what to do. Then her dog licked up the water for her!

2. Fran Miller doesn't want us to spill water.

   Fran Miller wants us to have fun reading this story.

School–Home Connection

Talk about a story that you and your child
know. Ask your child, "Why do you think the
author wrote the story?"

Name _____

▶ **Write a word from the box to complete each sentence.**

flown	roast	own
toast	grown	coast

_____

----

1. Dad made _____ and jam.

_____

----

2. Then we went to the _____.

_____

----

3. We like to _____ hot dogs.

_____

----

4. I can help make my _____ lunch.

_____

----

5. I have _____ up a lot.

School-Home Connection

Have your child read each completed sentence
aloud. Point to the word *flown* and ask your
child to use it in a sentence.

42

Practice Book
© Harcourt • Grade 1 • Book 3

Name _____

▶ **Choose a pair of homophones from the chart. Write sentences using the words correctly.**

buy	by
to	two
wax	whacks

1. _____

_____

_____

2. _____

_____

School-Home Connection

With your child, make flash cards of the words *by, buy, to, two, too, there, their,* and *they're.* Show each card, and have your child use the word correctly in a sentence.

43

Cut-Out/ Fold-Up Books

A Hen and Her Chicks

1

The hen needs some food.
She will not fly off and play.

3

The chicks lived with Mom.
Soon they grew to be hens.

8

Chip, chip! A chick is out. It
hops a little and smells the air.

6

Practice Book
© Harcourt • Grade 1 • Book 3 • Cut-Out/Fold-Up Book

"Cluck! Cluck!" says the hen.
Soon her eggs will hatch.

She checks the eggs and sits on them. When will the eggs hatch?

4

The hen calls to her friends.
"Come and see my little chicks!" 7

She watches the eggs. Chip, chip!
An egg cracks!

5

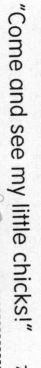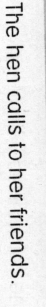

Stars by Carla

Carla makes stars at her house.
Then she puts them out to sell them. 3

— Fold —

— Fold —

Carla sells her stars.
That makes her feel happy.

8

"I make them," says Carla.
6 "You can hang them in your house."

47

2

It's time for Craft Day again.
The cars park at the big barn.

— Fold —

4

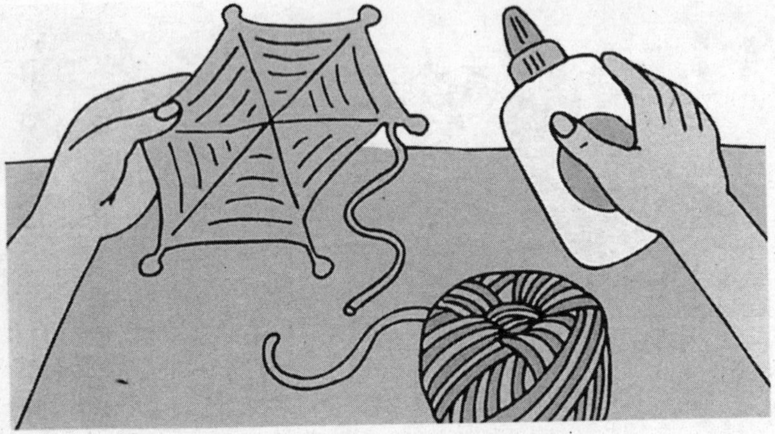

Sometimes the yarn slips
off a star. Carla fixes it.

— Fold —

"Can I get two? I know my
friend Bart will like one, too."

7

5

"Who makes the stars?
What are they for?"

48

Ducks in the Night

"Look, Dad! What's that?
It must want to come in."

— Fold — — Fold —

We had ducks in the house!
I am writing about that night.

8

The ducks have finished their
bath. Quick! Let's get them out!

6

49

My family is at home tonight. Mom

2 makes a quilt. Dad and I read books.

It's a bunch of ducks! What's this

4 all about? Mom drops her quilt.

Quack! Quack!

Soon they are all out.

7

They are quacking in the bathtub!
I think they grew up in a house.

5

Practice Book
© Harcourt • Grade 1 • Book 3 • Cut-Out/Fold-Up Book

Jump, Twirl, and Play

1

I always like to jump.
Can you jump like this?

3

— Fold —

— Fold —

Can you play the way we do?
Just don't twirl in the dirt!

8

Oh, no! We were twirling in the
dirt. Now the dirt is on us.

6

51

Please join in and play.
Do what I do. Jump this way.

Stand by me and take three
jumps. Then turn and twirl.

4

The dirt is on my skirt.
The dirt is on my shirt.

7

There's lots of room to twirl and
swirl. Jump this way and that.

5

Fold

Fold

Practice Book
© Harcourt • Grade 1 • Book 3 • Cut-Out/Fold-Up Book

A Pet for Me

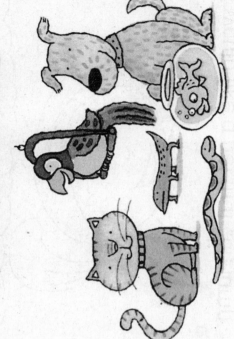

I can carry my little bug,

and it can jump far.

— Fold —

— Fold —

Yes! I can play with a frog. It can

jump in puddles. Hi, little pet!

8

A turtle is nice. It could play

with me, but it can't jump.

6

Practice Book
© Harcourt • Grade 1 • Book 3 • Cut-Out/Fold-Up Book

I would like a pet that can jump.

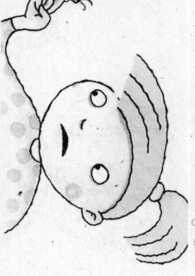

4 play with me.

other pet. I would like one that can

It's nice, but I am looking for some

— Fold —

— Fold —

Here is a pet you'll like.

It's home is very wet!

7

What about a turtle?

You can carry it to school.

5

54

Goat and Toad's Lunch

1

"What a load!" groaned Goat. "What did you pack for our lunch?"

3

Show the three surprises that you think were in the basket.

8

The basket was harder and harder to lift. "Come on," said Toad. "Carry it over the hill."

6

Practice Book
© Harcourt • Grade 1 • Book 3 • Cut-Out/Fold-Up Book

Goat met Toad for a picnic. "Let's go!"

2 said Toad. "I've packed lunch."

"I packed a surprise lunch," said Toad.

Goat and Toad went down the road.

4 The sun glowed.

"I can't go any farther," said Goat.
"This is the best spot. Let's eat,"
said Toad.

7

"What did you load into the
basket?" moaned Goat. "I put in
three nice things," croaked Toad.

5

Fold

Fold

Help Yourself

Characters

Horse 1 **Horse 2** **Man** **Bert** **Girl** **Brothers**

 It's raining! I just felt a drop on my head.

 We are not far from an inn.

 We need to stop there. I feel hungry for some good oats.

 You're always hungry!

 Why are the animals tossing their heads like that?

 I think they felt the rain. Let's go! We are not far from a nice inn!

 Watch out for that mud!

 What mud?

 Oh, no! That mud!

Readers' Theater
© Harcourt • Grade 1 • Book 3

Let's go! We can't stop here.

I think we're stuck in the mud!

Let's go! Tug harder, animals!

We're tugging! We're tugging!

I don't think he knows what
you're saying.

Bert, get out and tug on the animals
to get them going.

Don't tug on us. We are not stuck.
The wagon is stuck!

Come along, animals. I'll tug on you,
and you'll tug on the wagon.

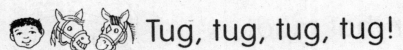 Tug, tug, tug, tug!

Let's go! Let's go!

No good. No good.

 You look stuck!

 Where did you come from?

 Where did they come from?

 That is our family's farm over there. Here are my brothers.

 Hi!

 How lucky that you showed up! Would you help us, please?

 We could use some new people to help.

 Yes, we can all help.

 You go to the back. I will tug on the animals. They will tug on the wagon.

 Let's go! Let's go!

 Tug, Tug, Tug, Tug!

 Work, work, work, work!

 No good. No good.

Readers' Theater
© Harcourt • Grade 1 • Book 3

 Are there more people in your family who could help?

Please don't go back to your farm yet. There is one other thing we did not do yet.

 What?

I could get down and help, too.

That could work.

Let's do it! I will help in the back.

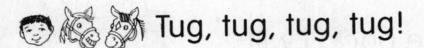 Tug, tug, tug, tug!

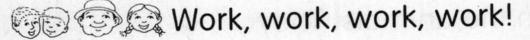 Work, work, work, work!

It's going!

Sometimes the person missing from the job is you.

Let's get to the inn!

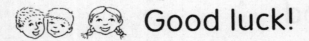 Good luck!

Readers' Theater
© Harcourt • Grade 1 • Book 3

Name _____

▶ **Read the selection. Then write 1, 2, 3,**
or 4 in front of each sentence to tell the
order in which events happen.

Market Day

My family grows apples. We sell them at the market.
We get there when the sun is coming up. Dad sets up
our booth so that it looks nice. People come from all over
to buy things. Many people walk by our booth. I help
sell the apples. People give me money. Then I give them
a bag of apples. I like to know that people will eat our
apples at home. After the market closes we go home.
My mom always gives me some of the money we make.
Market day is the best day of the week.

_____ People give me money.

_____ After the market closes we go home.

_____ I give them a bag of apples.

_____ Dad sets up our booth so that it looks nice.

School–Home Connection

Talk about your child's morning routine.
Have your child tell the order in which he
or she does things.

Practice Book
© Harcourt • Grade 1 • Book 3

Name _____

▶ **Read the story. Circle the sentence that
tells the main idea of the story.**

1. Our grass grows very fast. My dad has to mow
it every week. I help him. I pick up branches or
rocks. He mows the yard in rows. I make sure
that he does not skip a row. The yard looks
nice after it is mowed.

Dad mows the yard in rows.

I help Dad mow the yard.

2. My mom and I have a garden. Gardens need a lot of
work. The plants need water every day. It is my job to
feed them. My mom makes sure there
are no bugs on the plants. We have to
cover the plants if it gets cold. I like
working in the garden with my mom.

Plants need water every day.

I like working in the garden with my mom.

 **School–Home Connection**

Read each story with your child. Together, think
of a good title for each one that tells what the
story is mainly about.

62

Name _____

▶ **Read the sentences. Then tell how the birds and sea oats are the same.**

Some birds live along the shore. They make their nests in the flat sand. They eat small fish.

Sea oats grow along the shore. Their roots keep the sand from washing into the sea. They have seeds that blackbirds like to eat.

I. You can find birds and sea oats along the

_____

- -

_____ .

▶ **Now tell how the birds and sea oats are different.**

_____

- -

2. Birds are _____ .

_____

- -

3. Sea oats are _____ .

School–Home Connection
Ask your child to think of other ways the birds
and sea oats are alike and different.

63

Practice Book
© Harcourt • Grade 1 • Book 3

Be Strong

Book 1-4

▶ **Circle the word that has the long <u>e</u> sound, as in <u>wheel</u>. Write the word to complete the sentence.**

We   They

_____
- - - - - - - - - - - - - - - - -

1. _____ are digging in the garden.

like   eat

_____
- - - - - - - - - - - - - - - - -

2. Kim will _____ all her lunch.

sleep   rest

_____
- - - - - - - - - - - - - - - - -

3. I _____ in my bed.

peach · food

_____
- - - - - - - - - - - - - - - - -

4. This is a _____.

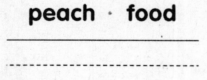

good   green

_____
- - - - - - - - - - - - - - - - -

5. Kathleen sees a _____ frog.

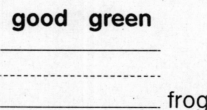

 School–Home Connection

Have your child read each sentence aloud to you. Ask your child to think of other words with the long e sound, as in *we*.

2

Name _____

▶ **Read the Spelling Words. Then write each word in the group where it belongs.**

Words with Long e

_____ _____

_____ _____

_____ _____

_____ _____

_____ _____

Words without Long e

_____ _____

_____ _____

_____ _____

Spelling Words

me
see
feet
seat
mean
team
slow
road
our
over

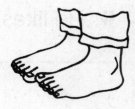

3

► **Write a word from the box to complete each sentence.**

| sweep | dream | reach | beach | sheep |

1. I _____ for an apple.

2. Robert has a _____.

3. Russ has a pet _____.

4. He likes to _____.

5. She is playing on the _____.

School–Home Connection

Write the sentence, *"We need peas."* Ask your child to read the sentence and tell how the words are alike and different.

4

▶ **Write a word from the box to complete each sentence.**

| door | hurry | mother | dear |
| should | sky | told | |

_____

1. My _____ and I are going to the park.

_____

_____

2. Mom locks the _____ before we go.

_____

_____

3. I _____ my friends we'd be there soon.

_____

_____   _____

4. We _____ _____ to get there.

_____

_____

5. The _____ is getting dark.

Practice Book
© Harcourt • Grade 1 • Book 4

▶ **Look at the picture that shows what happened. Then circle the sentence that tells why it happened.**

What Happened?	Why Did It Happen?
1.	She likes to drink milk.
	She dropped the cup.
	Milk was in the cup.
2.	His pillow was soft.
	He wanted to play.
	He was sick.
3.	The snow is cold.
	It's fun to play outside.
	The snow melted in the sun.
4.	They are sitting down.
	They liked the play.
	They will go home.

6

Name _____

▶ **Read the chart. Then write the contraction that completes each sentence.**

We	have	We've
You	are	You're
I	have	I've
We	are	We're
They	are	They're

1. Do you see them? _____ fishing.

2. I am big. _____ grown.

3. Please slow down. _____ going too fast.

4. I like Jeff. _____ good friends.

7

Name _____

▶ **Write two sentences that tell about things in the picture. Use describing words in each sentence.**

1. _____

_____

_____

2. _____

_____

_____

 **School–Home Connection**

Play *I Spy* with your child using words that tell about color, size, and shape. For example, *I spy something small, round, and yellow.* (a lemon)

Practice Book
© Harcourt • Grade 1 • Book 4

Name _____

► **Write the word from the box that completes the sentence.**

grain	wait	rain	ray
play	paint	gray	railroad

_____

- - - - - - - - - - - - - - - - - - - -

1. Jim and Fay _____ the barn red.

_____

_____

- - - - - - - - - - - - - - - - - - - -

2. Fay feeds _____ to the hens.

_____

_____

- - - - - - - - - - - - - - - - - - - -

3. Ducks and pigs _____ by the barn.

_____

_____

- - - - - - - - - - - - - - - - - - - -

4. The sky starts to turn _____.

_____

_____

- - - - - - - - - - - - - - - - - - - -

5. It starts to _____ outside.

School–Home Connection

Point to the words *wait*, *rain*, and *railroad*.
Have your child read each word aloud and use
it in a sentence.

9

▶ **Read the Spelling Words. Then write each word in the group where it belongs.**

Words with Long <u>a</u>

_____   _____

_____   _____

_____   _____

_____   _____

_____   _____

_____   _____

_____   _____

Words without Long <u>a</u>

_____   _____

_____   _____

_____   _____

_____   _____

Spelling Words

day
say
play
plain
rain
wait
feet
me
door
told

School–Home Connection

Have your child read each Spelling Word aloud. Talk about how the words are alike and how they are different. Start by comparing the words *day* and *say*.

10

► **Write the word from the box that completes the sentence.**

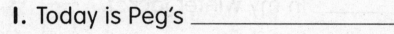

| way | sway | birthday | paint | rainbow | chain |

1. Today is Peg's _____.

2. Look at the pretty _____.

3. The trees _____ in the wind.

4. This is the shortest _____.

5. Doris needs yellow _____.

School–Home Connection

Have your child read each completed sentence
aloud. Point to the word *chain* in the box, and
ask him or her to use the word in a sentence.

11

▶ **Write a word from the box to complete the sentence.**

cool	dry	four	holes	move	place	warm

1. I stay _____ in my winter jacket.

2. My raincoat keeps me _____ when it rains.

3. My shorts keep my legs _____ in summer.

4. I dig _____ in the sand.

5. I like the _____ where I live.

Try This

Write a sentence that uses the word <u>four</u>.

School–Home Connection

Have your child read the sentences aloud.
Encourage him or her to write a new sentence
that includes two words from the box.

12

Name _____

▶ **The picture shows what happened.**
Write a sentence that tells why it happened.

He ran inside.

_____
- -
_____

She fed the rabbit.

_____
- -
_____

The paint spilled.

_____
- -
_____

 School–Home Connection

Talk about a story that your child enjoys. Have
your child tell you something that happened in
the story and explain why it happened.

13

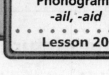

▶ **Cross out the word that is wrong.**
Write the correct word that ends with
ail or aid.

1. Fay reads her mall.

_____

- - - - - - - - - - - - - - - - - -

_____

2. Lee brings the pal to the barn.

_____

- - - - - - - - - - - - - - - - - -

_____

3. I see a snake.

_____

- - - - - - - - - - - - - - - - - -

_____

4. The man got pod.

_____

- - - - - - - - - - - - - - - - - -

_____

5. The dog wants to catch his tall.

_____

- - - - - - - - - - - - - - - - - -

_____

6. I have a brad.

_____

- - - - - - - - - - - - - - - - - -

_____

School–Home Connection
Say a sentence with one incorrect word. Have
your child say the sentence correctly.

14

Name _____

▶ **Use describing words to write a sentence about each picture. Write the sentences correctly.**

1.
_____
- - - - - - - - - - - - - - - - -
_____
_____
- - - - - - - - - - - - - - - - -
_____

2.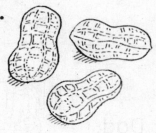
_____
- - - - - - - - - - - - - - - - -
_____
_____
- - - - - - - - - - - - - - - - -
_____

3.
_____
- - - - - - - - - - - - - - - - -
_____
_____
- - - - - - - - - - - - - - - - -
_____

School–Home Connection

Talk to your child, using words that describe
what things taste, smell, sound, and feel like
(*salty, fresh, squeaky, sharp*). Have your child
identify each describing word you use.

15

▶ **Write the word from the box that completes the sentence.**

came	gate	gave	lake
paste	scale	shade	take

_____
- - - - - - - - - - - - - - - -

1. I helped Dad paint the _____.

_____
- - - - - - - - - - - - -

2. Dad had to _____ a rest.

_____
- - - - - - - - - - - - - - - - -

3. I _____ over to sit near Dad.

_____
- - - - - - - - - - - - - - -

4. We sat in the _____.

_____
- - - - - - - - - - - -

5. Dad _____ me a cold drink.

Practice Book

Name _____

▶ **Read the Spelling Words. Then write each word in the group where it belongs.**

Words with Long <u>a</u>

_____   _____
- - - - - - - - - - - - - -   - - - - - - - - - - - - - -
_____   _____

_____   _____

_____   _____

_____   _____
- - - - - - - - - - - - - -   - - - - - - - - - - - - - -
_____   _____

_____   _____

_____   _____
- - - - - - - - - - - - - -   - - - - - - - - - - - - - -
_____   _____

_____
- - - - - - - - - - - - - -
_____

Word without Long <u>a</u>

_____
- - - - - - - - - - - - - -
_____

School–Home Connection

Write the Spelling Word *came*, and ask your child to change one letter to make the Spelling Word *game*. Repeat with *gate* (*late*) and *lake* (*take*).

17

▶ **Write the word from the box that
completes the sentence.**

chase	gave	late
name	paste	wake

1. It's time for my brother to _____ up.

2. This is not a day to sleep _____.

3. Last night, our uncle _____ us two
   hamsters.

4. I want to _____ my hamster Jake.

5. We watch them _____ each other.

School–Home Connection
Have your child read each completed sentence
aloud. Then write the words *cap* and *cape*.
Have your child read each word and draw a
picture for it.

18

Practice Book
© Harcourt • Grade 1 • Book 4

▶ **Write a word from the box to complete the sentence.**

around	found	near	tired
might	open	gone	hears

1. Snake _____ a loud crash.

2. He looks _____ the classroom.

3. Snake has _____ spilled paint.

4. It _____ take all night to clean up.

5. Snake cleans up. Now he is _____!

19

▶ **Read about each problem. Then circle the better solution.**

1. Kate's doll always gets lost. On some days, she finds it under the bed. On other days, she can't find it at all.

Kate could put the doll on a shelf.
Kate could give the doll to her sister.

2. Dave eats popcorn. He drops it all over the place. Popcorn is on the rug.

Dave should eat crackers, too.
Dave should clean up the popcorn.

3. Edmund's dog jumps up on people. It will not sit when Edmund tells it to sit. It barks all the time, too.

Edmund needs to get a bigger dog.
Edmund needs to train his dog.

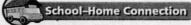

School–Home Connection

Talk about a problem in a story you and your child have read. Talk about how the problem was solved.

Practice Book
© Harcourt • Grade 1 • Book 4

▶ **Write the word from the box that completes the sentence.**

plane	shade	Shane
made	cane	lane

_____

1. A hat and a _____ are by the door.

_____

_____

2. Blake _____ a sandwich for lunch.

_____

_____

3. Blake will eat his sandwich on the _____.

_____

_____

4. They sit in the _____.

_____

_____

5. Uncle _____ waves at them.

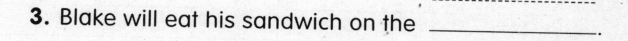

School–Home Connection

Have your child read each completed sentence aloud. Together, think of other words that end in -ane and -ade.

21

Name _____

▶ **Look at the picture. Write sentences that tell what you see. Use words that tell how many.**

1. _____
   _____

2. _____
   _____

3. _____
   _____

4. _____
   _____

5. _____

Practice Book
© Harcourt • Grade 1 • Book 4

Name _____

▶ **Cross out the word that is wrong. Write the correct word.**

1.
_____
- - - - - - - - - - - - - - - - - - - -
He will bit _____ the apple.

2.
_____
- - - - - - - - - - - - - - - - - - - -
I have a kit _____.

3.
_____
- - - - - - - - - - - - - - - - - - - -
A clock tells the tim _____.

4.
_____
- - - - - - - - - - - - - - - - - - - -
He will rid _____ the bus.

5.
_____
- - - - - - - - - - - - - - - - - - - -
They will hid _____ from him.

23

Name _____

▶ **Read the Spelling Words. Then write each word in the group where it belongs.**

Words with Long i

_____   _____
-----------------------   -----------------------
_____   _____
-----------------------   -----------------------
_____   _____
-----------------------   -----------------------
_____   _____
-----------------------   -----------------------
_____   _____

Words without Long i

_____   _____
-----------------------   -----------------------
_____   _____
-----------------------   -----------------------
_____   _____

Spelling Words

like
line
nine
mine
mile
while
take
came
gone
near

School–Home Connection

Have your child read each Spelling Word aloud.
Ask him or her what vowel sound is in each
word and what letters stand for the sound.

24

▶ **Look at the picture. Write a word from the box to complete each sentence.**

| kite | smile | five | time | slide |

_____
----

1. Carl will _____ down.

_____
----

2. It's _____ to eat dinner.

_____
----

3. Miles will be _____ on his birthday.

_____
----

4. I _____ when I am happy.

_____
----

5. Scott likes to fly his _____.

School–Home Connection

With your child, think of words that rhyme with each word in the box.

25

Name _____

▶ **Write a word from the box to complete each sentence.**

| because | light | right | Those | walked |

1. Skunk and Duck _____ to the game.
   _____

2. They sat _____ next to Hen and Eagle.

3. The baseball bats were not _____.

4. Eagle clapped _____ a player hit the ball.

5. "_____ players run so fast!" Hen said.

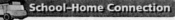
26

Practice Book
© Harcourt • Grade 1 • Book 4

▶ **Read about each problem. Then circle the better solution.**

1. Kim is cleaning her room. She put all her things in the box. Now she can't shut the lid.

Kim could take some things out.
Kim could stop cleaning her room.

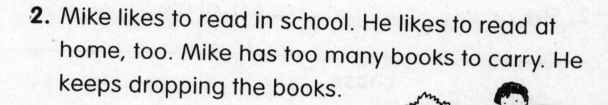

2. Mike likes to read in school. He likes to read at home, too. Mike has too many books to carry. He keeps dropping the books.

Mike could read the books.
Mike could get a backpack.

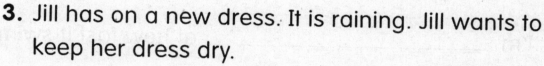

3. Jill has on a new dress. It is raining. Jill wants to keep her dress dry.

Jill could put on her raincoat.
Jill could sing about rain.

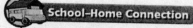
School–Home Connection

Talk about a story you and your child have
read in which there was a problem. Help your
child recall how the problem was solved.

27

▶ **Add -ed or -ing to make a new word.**
Write the word to complete the sentence.

wave

_____

1. My friend _____ to me.

_____

smile

_____

2. She _____ at me.

_____

chase

_____

3. I am _____ a little fish.

_____

surprise

_____

4. I'm _____ at how fast it swims.

_____

nibble

_____

5. The fish are _____ my feet!

School–Home Connection

Have your child read each completed sentence
aloud. Ask him or her which letter in each word
was dropped when –ed and –ing were added.

28

Name _____

▶ **Complete the sentences with feeling words.**

_____

1. When I play, I feel _____ .

_____

2. When I get a gift, I am _____ .

_____

3. When I sing a song, I feel _____ .

▶ **Write sentences to describe each picture. Use feeling words.**

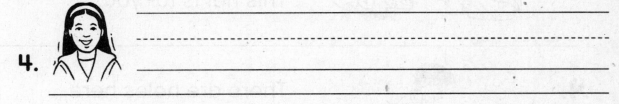

4. _____

_____

_____

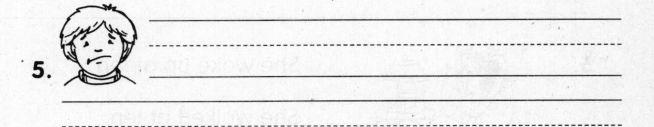

5. _____

_____

_____

_____

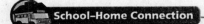

School-Home Connection

Ask your child to draw simple faces that show feelings. Then create sentences that describe those feelings.

29

▶ **Circle the sentence that tells about each picture.**

1.

   Kathleen hops in a game.

   Kathleen hopes to play well.

2.

   Mom has a soft brown robe.

   Mom has a brown stone.

3.

   This note is for you.

   This net is for you.

4.

   There are holes here.

   There are halls in here.

5.

   She woke up at ten.

   She walked at ten.

School–Home Connection

Have your child read each sentence aloud. Ask
which words have the long *o* sound as in *hope*.

30

Name _____

▶ **Read the Spelling Words. Then write each word in the group where it belongs.**

Words with Long o

_____   _____

_____   _____

_____   _____

_____   _____

_____   _____

Words without Long o

_____   _____

_____   _____

_____   _____

Spelling Words

home

hope

rope

rode

rose

those

like

nine

right

walk

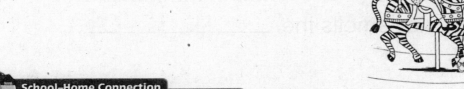

School–Home Connection

Have your child read each Spelling Word aloud. Talk about how the words are alike and how they are different. Start by comparing *home* and *hope*.

31

▶ **Complete each sentence with a word
that has the long o sound, as in rope.**

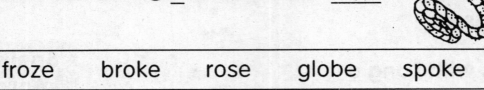

| froze | broke | rose | globe | spoke | hole |

1.

_____

Ann _____ the vase.

2.

_____

Do you see land on the _____?

3.

_____

The water in the pond _____.

4.

_____

He found a _____ in his sock.

5.

_____

Kay smells the _____.

Practice Book
© Harcourt • Grade 1 • Book 4

▶ **Write a word from the box to complete each sentence.**

brown	hello	loudly
love	pulled	city

_____

1. My family rode the bus to the _____.

_____

2. The bus driver said _____ to us.

_____

3. The bus _____ into the bus stop.

_____

4. I _____ to look in all the store windows.

_____

5. Cars honked their horns _____.

33

▶ **Read the story. Look at the picture.
Circle the sentence that draws a
conclusion about the story.**

1. Rose is very happy. She is thinking
   of the big cake she will have. Rose
   giggles when she thinks about the
   gifts she will open.

Rose must feed her cat.

It is Rose's birthday.

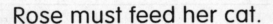

2. Kevin wore his green shirt to school.
   He put on green socks, too. Kevin
   wants a green rug for his room.

Kevin likes green.

Kevin likes frogs.

School–Home Connection

Give your child some clues about someone
or something in the house. Ask your child to
name the person or thing. Then have your
child give you clues.

34

Name _____

▶ **Circle the word that completes the sentence. Then write the word.**

bone   bean

_____

- - - - - - - - - - - - - - - - - -

1. The dog has a _____.

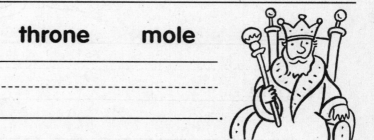

throne   mole

_____

- - - - - - - - - - - - - - - - - -

2. The king sits on his _____.

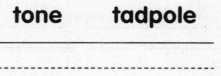

tone   tadpole

_____

- - - - - - - - - - - - - - - - - -

3. I see a little _____.

heal   hole

_____

- - - - - - - - - - - - - - - - - -

4. Ben is digging a _____ for his plant.

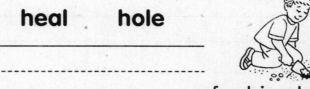

stone   stain

_____

- - - - - - - - - - - - - - - - - -

5. She is painting on the _____.

School–Home Connection

Together, think of other words that end in *one* and *ole*.

35

Practice Book
© Harcourt • Grade 1 • Book 4

▶ **Look at the picture. Write sentences that compare the animals. Use words that end in er and est.**

_____

1. _____

_____

_____

2. _____

_____

_____

3. _____

_____

_____

School–Home Connection

Write the words *tall*, *taller*, and *tallest*. Have your child read each word and then draw a picture that illustrates it.

Practice Book
© Harcourt • Grade 1 • Book 4

Name _____

▶ **Write the words where they belong
in the puzzle.**

cage	bridge	mice
pages	prince	space

Practice Book
© Harcourt • Grade 1 • Book 4

Name _____

▶ **Read the Spelling Words. Then write each word in the group where it belongs.**

Words with <u>c</u>

_____   _____
- - - - - - - - - - - - - - -   - - - - - - - - - - - - - - -
_____   _____

_____
- - - - - - - - - - - - - - -
_____

Words with <u>g</u>

_____   _____
- - - - - - - - - - - - - - -   - - - - - - - - - - - - - - -
_____   _____

_____
- - - - - - - - - - - - - - -
_____

Words without <u>c</u> or <u>g</u>

_____   _____
- - - - - - - - - - - - - - -   - - - - - - - - - - - - - - -
_____   _____

_____   _____
- - - - - - - - - - - - - - -   - - - - - - - - - - - - - - -
_____   _____

Spelling Words

ice
nice
race
page
edge
large
home
those
love
hello

School–Home Connection

Have your child circle the *d* in the word spelled
with *dge*. (*edge*) Then ask him or her to put a
checkmark by all the words that end in silent e.
(all words except *hello*)

38

Name _____

▶ **Write the word from the box that completes the sentence.**

stage	danced	fudge
center	gentle	circus

_____

1. Ginger went to a _____ with her dad.

_____

2. They ate _____ at the show.

_____

3. The show was in the _____.

_____

4. The people were on the _____.

_____

_____

5. People _____ on a wire.

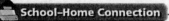

School–Home Connection

Have your child read each completed sentence
aloud. Then ask him or her to write a sentence
using the word *gentle*.

39

▶ **Write a word from the box to complete the sentence.**

eyes	listen	visitor	remembered
become	talk	busy	high

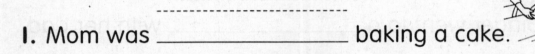

_____
- - - - - - - - - - - - - - - - - - - -

1. Mom was _____ baking a cake.

_____
- - - - - - - - - - - - - - - - -

2. She put the cake up _____ to cool off.

_____
- -

3. Spot had _____ excited about the cake.

_____
- - - - - - - - - - - - - - - - - - - -

4. Just then, a _____ rang the doorbell.

_____
- -

5. Mom _____ Spot. It was too late!

School–Home Connection

Have your child read each completed sentence aloud. Together, make up sentences for the unused words in the box.

Practice Book
© Harcourt • Grade 1 • Book 4

▶ **Read the story. Look at the picture.
Circle the sentence that draws a conclusion
about the story.**

1. Jade feeds Hank, her hamster, and gives
   him fresh water. When Hank is asleep,
   she reads about cats and dogs.

   **Hank reads many books.
   Jade likes animals very much.**

_____

2. Tim and Neal jump into the water. It is
   cold! Dennis goes down the slide. "Neal,
   I like to play in your pool!" Dennis says.

   **The boys are swimming at Neal's house.
   Neal and his friends can't swim well.**

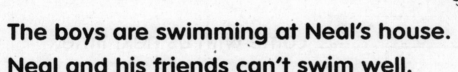

_____

3. Nick and Dad hang a note at the store.
   The note says Lost cat, black with white
   feet. Nick says to Dad, "I hope he will
   be found. I miss him so much."

   **Nick does not like cats.
   Nick feels sad.**

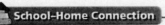

School-Home Connection

Talk with your child about the answer that he
or she chose for each story. Ask your child to
explain some of the clues that helped him or
her choose the answer.

41

Name _____

▶ Write the contraction that completes the sentence.

can't	didn't	We'll
Mom's	Dad's	He'll

_____
- - - - - - - - - - - - - - - - - - -

1. _____ go to the lake to camp.

_____

_____
- - - - - - - - - - - - - - - - - - -

2. My friend _____ come with us.

_____

_____
- - - - - - - - - - - - - - - - - - -

3. _____ come with us next time.

_____

_____
- - - - - - - - - - - - - - - - - - -

4. _____ packing the bags.

_____

_____
- - - - - - - - - - - - - - - - - - -

5. _____ taking the bags to the car.

Practice Book
© Harcourt • Grade 1 • Book 4

▶ **Draw pictures to show two meanings
of each word. Choose one meaning,
and write a sentence that shows it.**

1. bump

2. wave

School–Home Connection

With your child, think of sentences for two
meanings of the word *watch*. Have your child
draw a picture for each meaning of the word.

Practice Book
Harcourt • Grade 1 • Book 4

Cut-Out/
Fold-Up
Books

Can I Keep Him?

— Fold —

"Mother told me I could keep one.
I will keep this one," said Jean.

— Fold —

"Hurry Patch," said Doreen, "let's

8 go home. I'll feed you a treat."

"Dad, may I keep him?" asked
Doreen. "Yes," said Dad.
"You need a pet."

6

45

Practice Book

© Harcourt • Grade 1 • Book 4 • Cut-Out/Fold-Up Book

Jean saw two cats by her house.
They did not have a home.

"This is a nice cat, too. I should
ask Doreen if she wants a cat."

— Fold —

— Fold —

"He needs a name," said Dad.
"Let's call him Patch."

7

Doreen wants the cat. "Oh, dear!"
Doreen said. "I hope my dad will
let me keep him."

5

4

Work, Then Play

Mouse said she could not play.

She had to make a place to live.

© Harcourt • Grade 1 • Book 4 • Cut-Out/Fold-Up Book

— Fold —　　　　　　　— Fold —

Then the two friends played

8　all day.

"Make a warm, dry home.

6　Then you may play."

One warm day, Frog wanted to play with Mouse.

There were just four more days until winter. Soon it would be very cool outside.

Frog helped Mouse make her home. At last, her home was finished.

Her Dad said, "Mouse, you must make a winter home."

Fold

Fold

— Fold —

— Fold —

People like to watch the players
step up to the plate and hit the ball.

8   CRACK!

People in many lands play the
game. They play in the same way—

6   with a ball, a bat, and a mitt.

49

People play baseball in many places.

To play the game, you need only a ball, a bat, a mitt, and a big place to play.

2

The game began in the U.S.A.

First, it was called town ball.

Then it became baseball.

4

People might get tired when they play baseball. You have to run around a lot.

7

5

© Harcourt • Grade 1 • Book 4 • Cut-Out/Fold-Up Book

Bird Tales

Fold

One bird finds worms. Those worms are good for dinner.

Fold

Four white birds think about the new tales they will hear.

8

He wants to fly away again. Where will he go?

6

Practice Book
© Harcourt • Grade 1 • Book 4 • Cut-Out/Fold-Up Book

2

Five white birds live in the same nest. They get along because they're friends.

4

One bird tells tales about the places he has seen.

— Fold —

— Fold —

7

He doesn't know. He will come right back to tell more tales.

The others like to hear his tales. They smile because his tales are good.

5

Bad Dog!

1

"Hello," said Jake. "Do you want toast with jam?"

3

Bones ate up the toast and jam. All I got was a mess to clean up!

8

"I hope you will get down now, Bones!" said Jake.

6

53

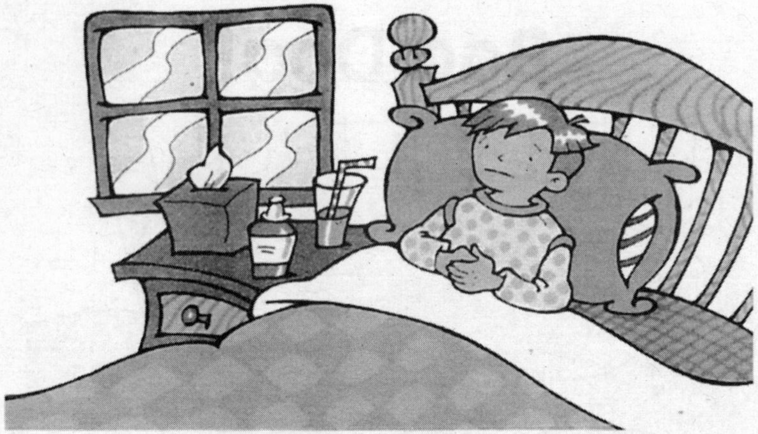

2

When I woke up, I felt sick.
My nose hurt. I had a bad cold.

4

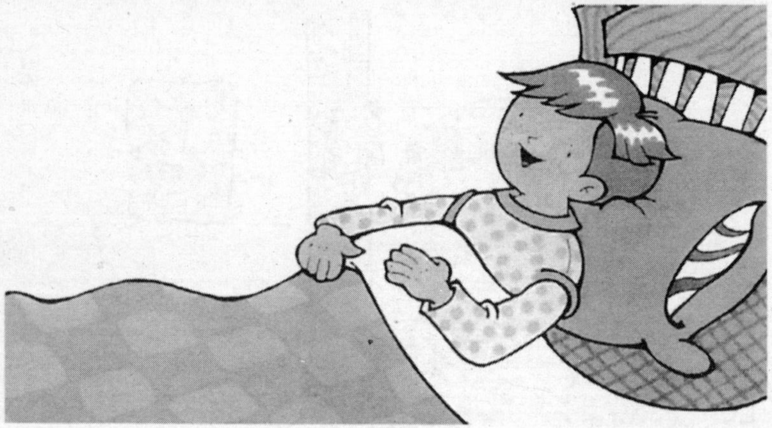

"Yes, I'd love toast with jam,"
I said.

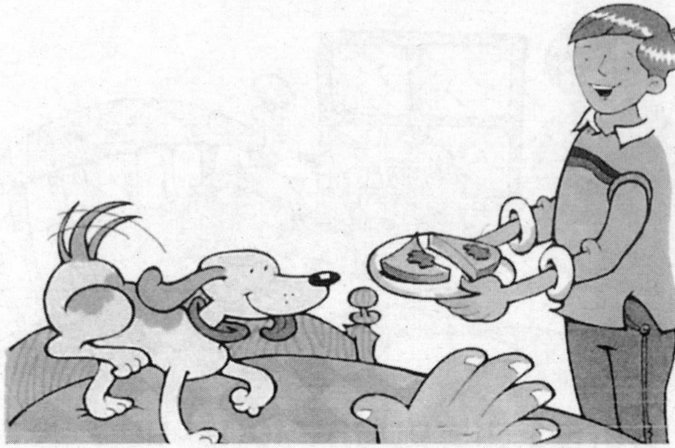

Bones jumped and poked around.
Then he barked loudly.

7

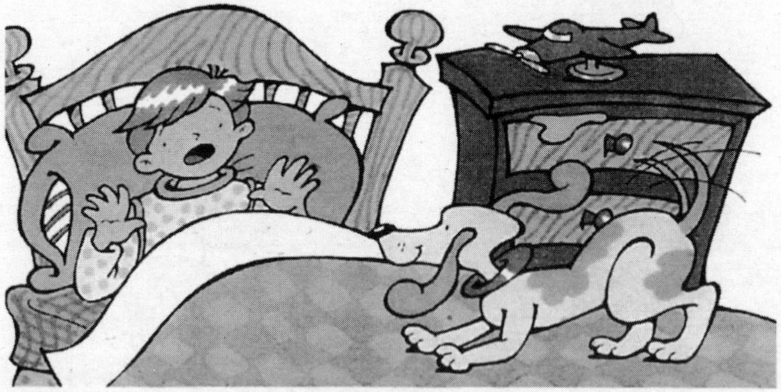

My dog, Bones, jumped up and pulled
the blanket. "No!" I said loudly.

5

The Old Bridge

1

"Let's try to cross the old bridge," said the little goat to the larger goats.

"No!" they said. "Rage won't let us!"

3

By now, the little goat had crossed the bridge. "Good-bye, Rage!" he called.

"Have fun fixing your bridge!"

8

"Just look at this rail," said the little goat. "It's not safe."

6

Practice Book

© Harcourt • Grade 1 • Book 4 • Cut-Out/Fold-Up Book

2

Rage sat on his old bridge.
"Listen, everyone! This is my bridge.
I will let no one cross it!"

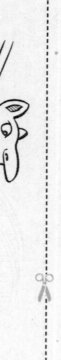

4 "Let's talk, Rage," said the little goat.
"You need to fix your bridge." "I do not!"
yelled Rage. "Go away!"

Fold

7

"Open your eyes, Rage! Look at this
large space in the center."

5

"This bridge has become old," said
the little goat. "Look at this edge.
It needs paint."

Practice Book

© Harcourt • Grade 1 • Book 4 • Cut-Out/Fold-Up Book

The Princess and the Peas

Narrator   **King Jack**   **Queen Jane**

Prince Ken   **King Dan**   **Princess Pam**

Narrator: In a land far away lived Queen Jane and King Jack. They were always looking for new friends for their son, Prince Ken.

Prince Ken: My friends must be smart and kind. They must also have good manners.

King Jack: We want you to have good manners, too.

Narrator: One day the doorbell rang. Prince Ken opened the door. The visitors were King Dan and Princess Pam.

King Jack: Hello! Please come in.

King Dan: What a lovely, warm place you have here.

Readers' Theater
© Harcourt • Grade 1 • Book 4

Queen Jane: King Dan has very nice manners. Let's see if Princess Pam does, too.

Princess Pam: My mother asked me to bring you these flowers, Queen Jane.

Queen Jane: Thank you! They are so pretty!

Narrator: The king and queen invited King Dan and Princess Pam to stay for dinner.

Queen Jane: Does Princess Pam like peas, King Dan?

King Dan: No, but I love peas. Peas with dinner will be fine.

Readers' Theater
© Harcourt • Grade 1 • Book 4

Narrator: At dinner, everything was going very well.

Queen Jane: Would you like some milk, Princess Pam?

Princess Pam: Yes, please.

King Jack: Would you like more hot dogs, Princess Pam?

Princess Pam: No, thank you. I'm full, but they were very good, sir.

Queen Jane: You have such nice manners!

Narrator: The queen was watching to see if Princess Pam would try the peas. A person with good manners tries a bite of everything.

Princess Pam: Prince Ken, do you play basketball?

Prince Ken: Yes, I do! Do you play, too?

Readers' Theater
© Harcourt • Grade 1 • Book 4

Princess Pam: I'm on a team.

Prince Ken: We should play a game after dinner.

Princess Pam: I would love to!

Narrator: Just then Princess Pam ate some peas.

King Jack: She's eating some peas!

Queen Jane: You don't like peas, but you still ate some!

King Jack: At last we've found the right friend for our son!

Prince Ken: Yes! Princess Pam is smart, kind, and she has good manners.

Princess Pam: Thank you! Would you like to play basketball now, Prince Ken?

Prince Ken: Yes! Let's go.

Narrator: That's how the princess who ate peas became Prince Ken's best friend.

Name _____

▶ **The picture shows what happened.**
Circle the sentence that tells why it
happened.

What Happened?	Why Did It Happen?
1. 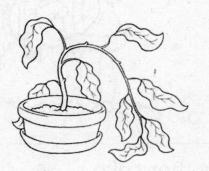	The plant needed water. The plant is sleeping. The plant is hiding.
2. 	The mouse is too large. The cage door was left open. The mouse is going home.
3. 	He liked the milk. He fell down. He drank too fast.

School–Home Connection

Talk about a story that you and your child have
read. Have your child tell something that happened
in the story and explain why it happened.

61

Name _____

▶ **Read the sentence and look at the picture. Circle the sentence that draws the correct conclusion.**

1. The children made a snowman.

It is summer.

It is winter.

---

2. Sue blows out the candles on her cake.

It is Sue's birthday.

Sue is sad today.

---

3. Mom picked up the phone and said, "Hello."

The phone was ringing.

The doorbell was ringing.

School–Home Connection

Ask your child what clues led to each of his or her conclusions.

62

Practice Book
© Harcourt • Grade 1 • Book 4

▶ **Look at the pictures and read the sentences. Complete the sentence that follows. Tell how the cats are alike.**

Ed's cat likes to take naps.
It sleeps on the floor.
It purrs a lot.

Maria's cat likes to nap, too.
It sleeps in her lap.
It does not purr very much.

1. Ed's cat and Maria's cat like _____

_____

_____

▶ **Now tell how the cats are different.**

2. Ed's cat sleeps _____

3. Maria's cat sleeps _____

School–Home Connection

Ask your child to name another way the cats are different.

63

Joyful Noise

Book 1-5

Name _____

▶ **Circle the sentence that tells about the picture.**

1. She thinks the doll is cute.

    She thinks the doll is cut.

2. We like to go swimming in the tub.

    We like to go swimming in June.

3. The cold cup is melting in the heat.

    The ice cube is melting in the heat.

4. She shows us a cobweb.

    She shows off her costume.

5. The tube is not empty.

    The tub is not empty.

School–Home Connection

Have your child read each sentence aloud. Ask
which words have the long *u* sound as in *cute*.

2

Name _____

▶ Read the Spelling Words. Then write each word in the group where it belongs.

Words with <u>u</u>

_____   _____
- - - - - - - - - - - - - - - - - -   - - - - - - - - - - - - - - - - - -
_____   _____
- - - - - - - - - - - - - - - - - -   - - - - - - - - - - - - - - - - - -
_____   _____
- - - - - - - - - - - - - - - - - -   - - - - - - - - - - - - - - - - - -
_____   _____
- - - - - - - - - - - - - - - - - -   - - - - - - - - - - - - - - - - - -
_____   _____

Words without <u>u</u>

_____   _____
- - - - - - - - - - - - - - - - - -   - - - - - - - - - - - - - - - - - -
_____   _____
- - - - - - - - - - - - - - - - - -   - - - - - - - - - - - - - - - - - -
_____   _____

Spelling Words

use
cute
cube
tube
tune
rule
nice
large
hear
talk

School–Home Connection

Have your child read each Spelling Word aloud. Ask him or her to point to the Spelling Words that end with a silent e.

Practice Book
© Harcourt • Grade 1 • Book 5

Name _____

▶ **Look at each picture. Write the word from the box that completes the sentence.**

use	rude	cute	flute	cube	mule

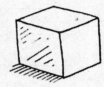

1. The block is the shape of a _____ .

2. Jake plays the _____ well.

3. The _____ will not get up.

4. She will _____ the brush.

5. He holds the _____ kitten.

School–Home Connection

Write the words *hug* and *huge*. Have your
child read the words aloud. Talk about how
the words are alike and different.

4

Practice Book
© Harcourt • Grade 1 • Book 5

▶ **Write the word from the box to complete the sentence.**

clear	color	good-bye	hair
kinds	toes	only	

1. We saw all _____ of animals.

2. A cat was licking between her _____ .

3. I saw fish in a _____ tank.

4. Dad liked the green _____ of the little bird.

5. I saw _____ one cat.

Try This

Write a sentence using a word from the box.

 School–Home Connection

Have your child read the words and sentences
aloud. Encourage your child to write other
sentences using the words.

5

▶ **Read the sentences. Circle the sentence that tells the main idea.**

1. Sam likes to play baseball with his friends. He can throw and catch the ball. When it is his turn to hit, the pitcher throws him the ball. He hits the ball with his bat and runs to first base. Sam is a good baseball player.

Sam likes playing baseball.

Sam has many friends.

2. Jan is going to the pond with her mom. She has her ice skates, her hat, and her scarf. She walks in the snow. She sees her friend Nick. They put on their skates and lace them up. It's time to have fun!

It is hard to walk in snow.

Jan is going ice skating.

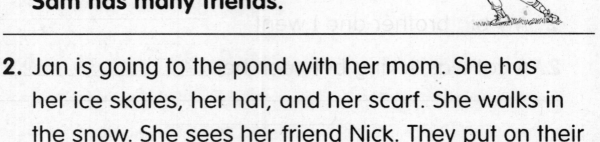

3. Jane and her family like to go to the lake. They swim in the water. Jane likes to float on her raft. Her dad drives the boat. They spend lots of time fishing on the dock. Trips to the lake are fun.

Jane and her family have fun at the lake.

Swimming is fun.

School–Home Connection

Talk about something you did at home. Ask your child to tell the main idea of what took place.

6

Practice Book
© Harcourt • Grade 1 • Book 5

Name _____

Phonics: Inflections
-*ed*, -*ing* (drop e)
Inflections -*ed*,
-*ing*

Lesson 25

▶ **Add ed or ing to the word. Write the new word in the sentence. Remember to drop the e or double the last letter.**

_____

1. I _____ my mom and dad good-bye.

   hug

_____

2. My big brother and I went _____ .

   hike

_____

3. We _____ at the stars last night.

   gaze

_____

4. Today, we will be _____ up rocks.

   dig

_____

5. We are _____ lots of fun!

   have

 School–Home Connection

Point to the words *hug* and *hike*. Ask your
child to explain how each word changes when
ing or *ed* is added to it.

7

▶ **Use verbs from the box. Write sentences that tell what animals do.**

leap	jump	wiggle	lick
bite	paddle	swim	dive
slither	sleep	cuddle	gobble
flop			

1. _____

_____

_____

2. _____

_____

_____

3. _____

_____

_____

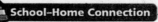
School–Home Connection

Say sentences aloud using interesting verbs
such as *wiggle, bump, stretch, crumple, freeze,*
and *shuffle.* Have your child identify the verb
in each sentence.

8

Practice Book
© Harcourt • Grade 1 • Book 5

▶ **Circle the word that completes the sentence. Then write the word.**

pea   pie   pay

_____

----

1. Beaver was eating some _____ .

_____

try   tray   tie

_____

----

2. "May I _____ some of that?" asked Turtle.

_____

mitt   mate   might

_____

----

3. "You _____ not like it," said Beaver.

_____

Way   Why   We

"_____

----

4. _____ not?" asked Turtle.

_____

may   me   my

_____

----

5. "I make _____ pies with mud," Beaver said.

9

Name _____

▶ **Read the Spelling Words. Then write each word in the group where it belongs.**

Words with i

_____   _____

_____   _____

_____   _____

_____   _____

_____

Words with y

_____   _____

_____

Words without i or y

_____   _____

_____   _____

_____

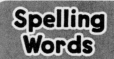

Spelling Words

my

try

tried

ties

light

might

use

rule

hair

color

 **School–Home Connection**

Have your child read each Spelling Word
aloud. Talk about different ways to spell the
sound /ī/.

 10

Name _____

▶ **Write the word from the box that completes the sentence.**

cried	high	lights	night
sight	sky	tried	why

_____

1. Last _____, we looked at the stars.

_____

2. It was fun to see their twinkling _____.

_____

3. "There's a falling star!" _____ Mom.

_____

4. "What a lovely _____!"

_____

5. She reached out and _____ to catch it.

School–Home Connection

Have your child read the words and sentences aloud. Encourage him or her to write additional sentences using the words *high* and *why*.

11

▶ **Write the word from the box that completes the sentence.**

climbed	earth	fooling	thought	table

1. We will read about the _____.

2. Luke _____ that he would like to read about that.

3. Mrs. Hill _____ up to get the globe.

4. She set the large globe on the _____.

5. Mrs. Hill was not _____ us when she told us the earth is round!

School–Home Connection

Point to each word in the box, and have your child use it in a sentence.

12

Practice Book
© Harcourt • Grade 1 • Book 5

Name _____

▶ **Read the story. Then circle the answer
to each question.**

The sun is shining on the creek. Beaver is cutting
down a small tree. He is making a nice home out of
sticks and branches.

Beaver hears some children playing nearby. Splash!
Beaver slaps his flat tail on the water. This tells all the
beavers to hide until the children go away.

Chomp, chomp! Nibble, nibble! Beaver must hurry.
At the end of the day, Beaver has a nice new home.

I. Who is this story about?

some children   Beaver   a tree

---

2. Where does this story happen?

at a creek   in a house   at a school

---

3. What is it about?

- Children like to play by creeks and look at beavers.

- Beavers can slap their tails on the water.

- Beaver works hard and makes a nice home.

School–Home Connection

Have your child read the story aloud. Talk
about what happens in the beginning, in the
middle, and at the end of the story.

Practice Book
© Harcourt • Grade 1 • Book 5

▶ **Look at the picture. Write the word from the box that completes the sentence.**

She'd	They're	He'd	You'd	We've	I've

1. _____ like to ride on the train.

2. _____ having fun sailing on the lake.

3. _____ lost my hamster.
Will you help me find it?

4. _____ like to swim
with the other children.

School–Home Connection
Ask your child to read one of the sentences he
or she completed. Then ask your child what
two words make up each contraction.

14

▶ **Use verbs from the chart to write sentences that tell about now.**

| plant | grow | fall | dig | pick |
| plants | grows | falls | digs | picks |

1. _____

_____

_____

2. _____

_____

_____

3. _____

_____

_____

School–Home Connection

With your child, make up sentences using the verbs *stamp*, *shake*, and *sweep*. Then ask your child to add *s* to each verb and use it in a new sentence.

15

► **Write the word from the box that
completes each sentence.**

tower	proud	crown
flowers	found	out

1. The queen put her _____ on.

2. She went _____ to find
the king.

3. The king could not be _____.

4. She went up in the _____.

5. She saw the king picking _____.

School–Home Connection

Have your child read each completed sentence
aloud. Point to the word *proud*, and ask your
child to use the word in a sentence.

Practice Book
© Harcourt • Grade 1 • Book 5

▶ **Read the Spelling Words. Then write each word in the group where it belongs.**

Words with <u>ow</u>

_____   _____
_____   _____
_____
_____

Words with <u>ou</u>

_____   _____
_____   _____
_____
_____

Spelling Words

how
cow
down
out
found
round
try
light
earth
table

Words without <u>ow</u> or <u>ou</u>

_____   _____
_____   _____
_____   _____

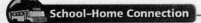

School–Home Connection

Ask your child to read aloud two pairs of Spelling Words that rhyme. (*how, cow; found, round*) Have your child think of words to rhyme with the other Spelling Words.

17

▶ **Write the words where they belong in the puzzle.**

couch	cow	house	flower
mouth	owl	tower	

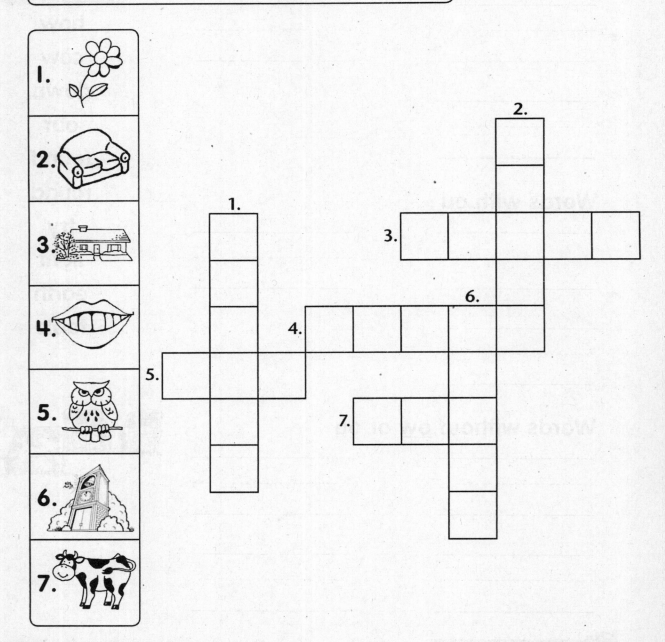

School–Home Connection

Write the words *blouse*, *growl*, *cloud*, and *round*. Say a clue for each word, and have your child point to the correct word.

Practice Book
© Harcourt • Grade 1 • Book 5

Name _____

▶ **Write a word from the box to complete each sentence.**

| answered | baby | heard | pools |
| done | pushed | together |

1. Mrs. Brown _____ the door.

2. We went to the park _____ .

3. Mrs. Brown's _____ went too.

4. I _____ Brad on the swing.

5. We _____ Brad giggle.

Practice Book
© Harcourt • Grade 1 • Book 5

▶ **Read the story. Then circle the best answer for each question.**

Butterfly woke up and said, "I am going on a trip to see my friends!" He packed a snack.

Up, up, up he flew. "Oh no!" Butterfly cried. "I forgot my map! How will I find my friends?"

Butterfly tried to think of what to do. He said, "I will look for the bright red flowers in their yard!" He saw the flowers. He flew down.

"Hi, Robin! I'm so glad to be here!" Butterfly called.

---

1. Who is this story about?

   Robin and Finch   Butterfly   birds

---

2. When does the story happen?

   at lunchtime   in the night   in the morning

---

3. What is the story about?

   Butterfly eats a snack.

   Butterfly wants to find his friends.

   Butterfly sets things up for a game.

 20

Name _____

▶ **Write the word from the box that completes each sentence.**

ground	town	round
sound	down	clown

_____
\- - - - - - - - - - - - - - - -

1. Ed dressed up like a _____ for my birthday.

_____
\- - - - - - - - - - - - - - - -

2. He jumped up and _____.

_____
\- - - - - - - - - - - - - - - -

3. He fell on the _____ and giggled.

_____
\- - - - - - - - - - - - - - - -

4. His dog played with a _____ ball.

_____
\- - - - - - - - - - - - - - - -

5. Ed is the best clown in _____!

School–Home Connection

Have your child read each completed sentence
aloud. Point to the word *sound*, and ask him or
her to say it in a sentence.

21

▶ **Write am, is, or are to complete each sentence.**

1. I _____ riding my bike.

2. Mom _____ riding her bike.

3. We _____ riding to the pond.

4. You _____ going too fast!

5. She _____ waiting for me.

 School–Home Connection

Help your child use *am*, *is*, and *are* correctly.
Say what you are doing—for example, *I am
cutting carrots. This carrot is long.* Have your
child create similar sentences.

Practice Book
© Harcourt • Grade 1 • Book 5

▶ **Circle the sentence that tells about each picture.**

1. The pets hurry to a field.
We're having a funny pet party.

_____

2. Annie's bunny has floppy ears.
The bunny finds pennies.

_____

3. Molly's puppy hurries to see the bunny.
The puppy smells plenty of daisies.

_____

4. Twenty pretty kittens take a nap.
Randy shows us a very sleepy kitty.

_____

5. Molly's frisky puppy wants to play.
The animals left a muddy mess.

_____

6. Ronnie is hungry for toast and jelly.
Everybody is happy about the party.

School–Home Connection
Ask your child to find all the words spelled
with *y* or *ie* and read them aloud.

23

Name _____

▶ **Read the Spelling Words. Then write each word in the group where it belongs.**

Words with y

_____   _____

_____   _____

_____   _____

_____   _____

_____

Spelling Words

funny

happy

story

stories

hurry

hurried

how

out

baby

done

Words without y

_____   _____

_____   _____

_____   _____

School–Home Connection

Have your child read each Spelling Word
aloud. Ask your child to change *story* to make
stories, and *hurry* to make *hurried*.

24

Practice Book

Name _____

▶ **Write the word from the box that
completes each sentence.**

sunny	windy	family
worry	field	hurried

_____

1. Angie and her _____ went on a picnic.

_____

_____

2. They went to a grassy _____.

_____

_____

3. It was a very _____ day.

_____

_____

4. Then it got rainy and _____.

_____

_____

5. They got their things and _____ home.

🖊 **Try This**

Draw a picture of you and your friends having a picnic.
Use the words in the box to write about the picture.

School–Home Connection

Have your child read each completed sentence
aloud. Ask him or her to tell which letters make
the long e sound in *field* and *sunny*. (*ie*, *y*)

Practice Book
© Harcourt • Grade 1 • Book 5

Name _____

▶ **Write a word from the box to complete
each sentence.**

| great | took | poured | almost |
| traveled | blue | able |

1. Betsy's mom and dad _____ her
on a trip.

2. They _____ to the seashore.

3. Betsy liked the sparkling _____ water.

4. Betsy _____ sand into a bucket.

5. Betsy was _____ to swim with her mom's help.

6. It was a _____ trip.

26

Name _____

▶ Read the story. Write three details about it.

Jimmy likes to make things out of blocks. He makes a small house. He uses red blocks for the walls. Jimmy uses some black blocks for the windows. The beds are made from blue blocks. Jimmy plays for a long time. He is proud of all the things he made with blocks.

_____

_____

_____

_____

_____

_____

School–Home Connection

Read the story with your child. Ask him or her to read the parts of the story that are not details about what Jimmy is making. (*Jimmy plays for a long time; He is proud. . . .*)

27

Name _____

Phonics: Inflections
-*ed*, -*er*, -*est*, -*es*
(change *y* to *i*)
Lesson 28

▶ **Read the words in the box. Look at the pictures. Write the word that completes each sentence.**

daisies	families	happier
hurried	worried	prettiest

1. Julie was _____ about her party.

2. "What if no one likes the _____ on the cake?"

3. All the kids _____ to see the cake.

4. They said it was the _____ cake they had ever had.

5. That made Julie feel much _____.

School–Home Connection

Ask your child to name the root word for each word in the box. *(daisy, family, happy, hurry, worry, pretty)*

28

Practice Book
© Harcourt • Grade 1 • Book 5

Name _____

▶ **Change each verb in the box to a verb
that tells about the past. Then choose one
verb and write a sentence about the past.**

1.	jump	------------------------
2.	move	------------------------
3.	want	------------------------
4.	walk	------------------------
5.	clean	------------------------
6.	pick	------------------------

7. _____

School–Home Connection

Have your child tell you about what he or
she did in school today. Encourage your child
to use words that tell about the past. For
example, *I watched the fish. I kicked the ball.*

29

▶ **Circle the sentence that tells about the picture.**

1. The boy has two boats.
   The boy is in the room.
   The boy has on boots.

2. Jenny stands by the pole.
   Jenny goes to the zoo.
   Jenny has lost a tooth.

3. The owl fools the moon.
   The owl flew to the moon.
   The owl hoots at the moon.

4. This bird eats with a spoon.
   This bird eats fish for food.
   This bird sits on a stool.

5. Mom reads the news at noon.
   Mom reads a book.
   Mom reads to a poodle.

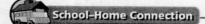
School–Home Connection
Ask your child to read each sentence aloud.
Have him or her underline the words that have
the vowel sound heard in *boot*.

Practice Book
© Harcourt • Grade 1 • Book 5

▶ **Read the Spelling Words. Then write each word in the group where it belongs.**

Words with oo

_____   _____
- - - - - - - - - - -   - - - - - - - - - - -
_____   _____

_____   _____
- - - - - - - - - - -   - - - - - - - - - - -
_____   _____

_____
- - - - - - - - - - -
_____

Spelling Words

boot

tooth

soon

noon

new

grew

story

hurry

great

took

Words without oo

_____   _____
- - - - - - - - - - -   - - - - - - - - - - -
_____   _____

_____   _____
- - - - - - - - - - -   - - - - - - - - - - -
_____   _____

_____
- - - - - - - - - - -
_____

 School–Home Connection

Have your child read each Spelling Word aloud. Write the words *book* and *booth*. Have your child change one letter in each word to make a Spelling Word (*took, tooth*).

Practice Book
© Harcourt • Grade 1 • Book 5

▶ **Write the word from the box that completes each sentence.**

blew	bloomed	roots	droopy
room	grew	noodle	cool

1. Oh, no! This plant looks _____.

2. It may need more _____ to grow.

3. I will water its _____.

4. Now I'll put it in a _____ spot.

5. The plant _____ so fast!

School–Home Connection
Ask your child to read each sentence aloud.
Together, think of other words with the vowel
sound spelled oo or ew, as in bloom or grew.

▶ **Write a word from the box to complete each sentence.**

| boy | building | tomorrow |
| toward | welcoming |

It's fun _____ things

out of clay. I like to make things with a

_____

_____ named Carl. He has such

_____

a _____ smile. When I carry my

_____

art _____ the table, I will not

_____

drop it. I will finish this _____.

Name _____

▶ **Read the story about the picnic.
Then answer each question.**

   Mom is taking my friends and me on a picnic. We are packing our food in a big cooler with some ice. Leslie and Mary pack ham and cheese sandwiches. Mom packs some apples. "Julie, don't forget to put in some water bottles!" Mom tells me. Now we are all set to go on our picnic.

1. What sandwiches will they eat? _____

_____

_____

_____

2. What fruit will they eat? _____

_____

_____

3. Who is going on the picnic? _____

_____

_____

School–Home Connection

Have your child read the story to you. Talk about the items that are being packed for the picnic. What would your child pack?

34

Practice Book
© Harcourt • Grade 1 • Book 5

▶ **Complete each sentence. Write the
contraction for the two words in the box.**

I	have

_____

- - - - - - - - - - - - - - - - - - - -

1. _____ been here for a long time.

can	not

_____

- - - - - - - - - - - - - - - - - - - -

2. I _____ wait much longer.

They	will

_____

- - - - - - - - - - - - - - - - - - - -

3. _____ be late for the play.

She	is

_____

- - - - - - - - - - - - - - - - - - - -

4. _____ acting like a butterfly.

We	are

_____

- - - - - - - - - - - - - - - - - - - -

5. _____ going to a party later.

School-Home Connection

Write the following contractions: *you'd,
you're, you'll.* Ask your child to tell you which
two words each contraction stands for. (*you
would; you are; you will*)

▶ **Write <u>was</u> or <u>were</u> on the lines to
complete the story.**

The house _____ messy. It _____ Mom's

birthday. She _____ still at work. Dad and Sandy

_____ cleaning. Arthur _____ making a

big cake. We _____ excited. Soon the house and

the cake _____ ready.

▶ **Use <u>was</u> or <u>were</u> to write a sentence about what
happened when Mom came home.**

_____

_____

_____

School–Home Connection

Encourage your child to use *was* to describe
something that one person was doing, and
were to describe something that two or more
people were doing.

36

Name _____

▶ **Write the word from the box that
completes the sentence.**

hold	kind	I'm
won't	tidy	open

_____

1. "Can you _____ the door?" asked Mom.

"_____

2. _____ happy to help," said Joan.

_____

3. "I'll be glad to _____ some bags, too."

_____

4. "That's very _____ of you," Mom said.

_____

5. "I _____ forget how you have helped me."

37

Name _____

▶ **Read the Spelling Words. Then write each word in the group where it belongs.**

Words with i

_____   _____
_____   _____
_____   _____
_____

Words with o

_____   _____
_____   _____
_____   _____
_____   _____

Words without i or o

_____
_____

🚌 **School–Home Connection**

Have your child read each Spelling Word aloud.
Write *kind* and *bold*, and have your child write
Spelling Words that rhyme with each one.

38

Practice Book

▶ **Write the word from the box that completes the sentence.**

kind	chosen	behind
tiger	nobody	title

_____
----

1. Janet had _____ a book to read.

_____

_____
----

2. She liked the _____ of the book.

_____

_____
----

3. The book was about a _____.

_____

_____
----

4. It was the _____ of book she liked to read.

Try This

Choose a word from the box. Write a sentence of your own.

School-Home Connection

Have your child read each completed sentence aloud. Ask him or her to write another sentence using one of the words from the box.

39

Name _____

▶ **Finish the sentences to tell about
yourself.**

1. When I get **ready** for school, I

_____

- - - - - - - - - - - - - - - - - - - -

_____ .

_____

2. I like to read **any** book that's about

_____

- - - - - - - - - - - - - - - - - - - -

_____ .

_____

3. I stand in the **front** of the mirror when I

_____

- - - - - - - - - - - - - - - - - - - -

_____ .

_____

4. There is **nothing** that I like more than

_____

- - - - - - - - - - - - - - - - - - - -

_____ .

_____

5. I say that I am **sorry** when I

_____

- - - - - - - - - - - - - - - - - - - -

_____ .

_____

School–Home Connection

Ask your child to read each sentence to you.
Talk about what it means to be *ready*.

40

Name _____

▶ **Read the story. Then circle the answer
to each question**

Jack and his friends are camping in the backyard. They
help set up the tent and then get inside. They have lots of
snacks. Jack tells a funny story about a rabbit he saw in
his backyard. It is dark outside, but they have flashlights.
The friends can't sleep. They hear a sound outside. Is it
the rabbit? No, it's only Mom bringing ice cream!

1. What is this story about?

going to the beach

camping in the backyard

fishing in a pond

_____

2. Who is this story about?

a rabbit

Mom

Jack and his friends

_____

3. Where and when does this story take place?

the backyard at night

school at lunchtime

Jack's bedroom in the morning

School–Home Connection

Talk about a story your child has read. Ask your
child to name the characters, setting, and plot
of the story.

41

▶ **Read the clues. Then write the words where they belong in the puzzle.**

| holds | gold | sold |
| cold | old | fold |

1. Mom ____ the baby.

2. It's not hot. It's ____.

3. My ring is made of ____.

4. I am 7 years ____.

5. I can ____ a shirt.

6. They ____ their house.

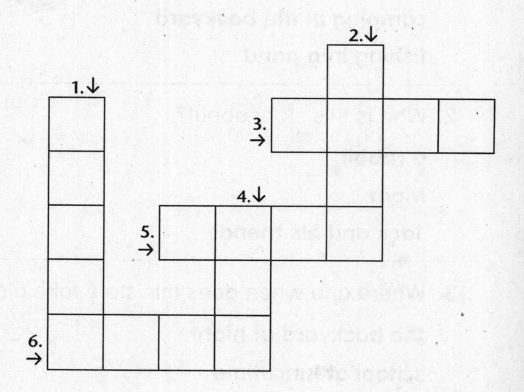

Name _____

▶ **Write go and went to complete
the story.**

Planning the Party

_____

Annie _____ to visit Liz last week. They

_____

planned a party. Yesterday, Liz _____ to

the store to buy milk and eggs. Today, Liz and Jan will

_____

_____ to Annie's house. They will make

cupcakes.

▶ **Now, imagine you were invited to the party. Write a
sentence to tell what you will do or what you did do.
Use go or went correctly.**

_____

_____

_____

_____

 School–Home Connection

Talk about where you and your child went
yesterday or last week. Then talk about where
you will go today or tomorrow.

43

Cut-Out/ Fold-Up Books

Mule Brings News

Fold

"I have some bad news, little moles," said Mule.

Fold

The moles jumped down into their hole. "Thanks for the news, Mule!"

8 they called.

"Why?" asked the moles. "What is

6 this bad news?"

45

2

Mule spotted three cute
moles beside a hole.

"We don't want to hear bad news,"
the moles said.

4

---Fold---

---Fold---

"The news is that a huge snake is
coming," Mule told them. "Find a
safe place to hide!"

7

Mule said, "I hate to be rude, but
there is no time to waste!"

5

46

Little Bird's Flight

"I will fly around the earth!"
thought Little Bird.

Fold

Little Bird found a
nice new home.

Little Bird flew for a long time.
The sky got lighter and brighter.

47

2

Little Bird thought it
was time to fly away.

4

The winter was very cold.
Other birds flew along with her.

Fold

Fold

7

The days got longer
and warmer.

5

Sometimes there was very little
to eat. Little Bird was hungry.

Practice Book
© Harcourt • Grade 1 • Book 5 • Cut-Out/Fold-Up Book

Bob Brown in Town

1

Bob made a list of things to buy.

Then he went to town.

3

Fold

The friends ate a fine lunch together. "It's nice to have lunch with an old friend," said Rose. "It's nice to have lunch with my new friends," said a baby butterfly.

8

The friends shopped around town together. When they were done they went to Bob's house.

6

49

Practice Book

© Harcourt • Grade 1 • Book 5 • Cut-Out/Fold-Up Book

2

Bob Brown was hungry.
He wanted to eat.

In town, he met Rose. "I heard you were in town," said Bob. "Can you have lunch with me today?"

4

Bob Brown used the food to make lunch. He even set out flowers!

7

"Yes," said Rose. "How nice of you to ask!"

5

Fold

Fold

Mike in the Sky

— Fold —

"Someday, I will be able to go up in the blue sky. I really want to try."

— Fold —

I LOVE TO FLY

Up in the blue sky, Mike wrote
"I love to fly!"

8

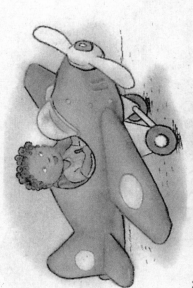

Mike dreamed that he got his wish. He got into a plane and took off!

6

2

Mike had a dream. He wanted to travel in a plane.

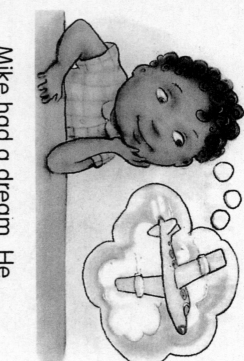

4

Mike went to school. He studied hard.

"This is great! It's easy! I can see trees and streams and fields!"

7

"Someday, I'm going to fly," he told his friends. "It's my dream."

5

At the Zoo

ZOO RACE

Fold

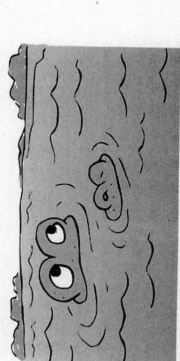

"Oh, boy! I am winning," she shouts.

Babs the baboon soon leads the way. 3

ZOO RACE

Who do you think will win?

8

Fold

Croc gets lost. "Oops! Now I won't

finish the race until tomorrow!"

he says.

6

The welcoming sign is up.

It is time for the race.

"On your mark. Get set. Go!"

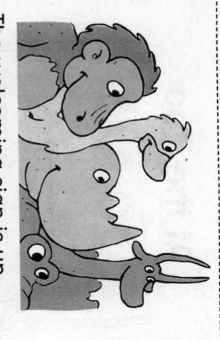

2

Ozzy runs like the wind. "I am just a few steps away from Babs," he says.

4

Bounder is running toward the finish line. "I hope that I will win!" says Bounder.

7

Richie is fast for his huge size. The ground shakes as he runs. "Here I come!" he calls.

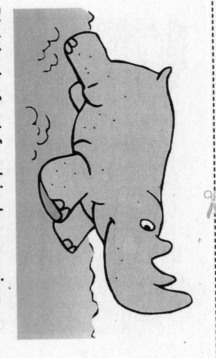

5

What Can I Do?

My building falls down. I don't want to play with blocks. There's nothing to play with!

"Find something new to do," says Mom.

3

What do you like to do on cold, rainy days?

8

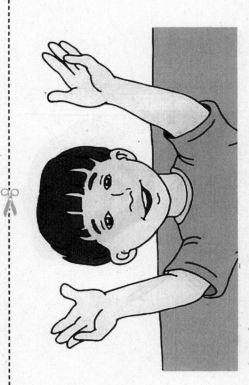

"Yes, I'm ready to help!"

Mom and I both like to bake.

6

It's rainy and cold, so I play inside.

2 I'm making a tall building with blocks.

I run like a wild animal. Mom
says, "Don't run any more."

4 "I'm sorry," I say.

Fold

This snack tastes really good! I hope
it's cold and rainy tomorrow. Then we
can bake again!"

7

"Are you ready to help with
the baking?" asks Mom.

5

Practice Book
© Harcourt • Grade 1 • Book 5 • Cut-Out/Fold-Up Book

The Thing Under the Bridge

Big Billy Goat
Middle Billy Goat

Little Billy Goat
Wind

Big Billy Goat: Look at the sun rise in the beautiful, blue sky.

Middle Billy Goat: Yes. It's a new day of eating grass.

Little Billy Goat: Today is just like yesterday. Tomorrow will be the same. Nothing ever changes.

Middle Billy Goat: Every day we eat grass and see the same things—

Big Billy Goat: the cool river,

Middle Billy Goat: the hill,

Little Billy Goat: the grass,

Big Billy Goat: the bridge,

Little Billy Goat: and all that yummy clover on the other side of the bridge.

Middle Billy Goat: If only we could cross the bridge.

Little Billy Goat: Why can't we cross the bridge?

57

Wind: Whooooooooooo! Whoooooooooooooooo!

Big Billy Goat: Can't you hear that sound? That's why we cannot cross the bridge!

Little Billy Goat: I think you are just fooling around! That sound might just be the wind.

Wind: Whooooooooooo! Whoooooooooooooooo!

Big Billy Goat: I think it heard you! Stand together so we will be safe!

Middle Billy Goat: It is very loud!

Big Billy Goat: Whatever it is, it must be big.

Wind: Whooooooooooo! Whoooooooooooooooo!

Little Billy Goat: The clover looks great. I can almost taste it from here.

Big Billy Goat: Where are you going? I thought I told you we can't go!

Middle Billy Goat: Come back!

Big Billy Goat: Oh, dear! I can't look.

Readers' Theater
© Harcourt • Grade 1 • Book 5

Middle Billy Goat: Is that Little Billy Goat walking toward the clover?

Big Billy Goat: No. It can't be.

Middle Billy Goat: He's climbing up the hill. I think he's eating the clover!

Big Billy Goat: Why is he rolling around on the ground like that?

Middle Billy Goat: I think he's very happy.

Big Billy Goat: That is not our Little Billy Goat. The thing under the bridge ate him all up!

Wind: Whoooooooooo! Whooooooooooooooo!

Middle Billy Goat: I don't think there is anything under the bridge!

Big Billy Goat: What?

Middle Billy Goat: I think it's only the wind!

Wind: Whooooooooooo!

Middle Billy Goat: I'm ready to go, too.

Big Billy Goat: Listen to me! Don't go! You will not be able to make it!

59

Middle Billy Goat: I'll see you on the other side!

Big Billy Goat: I see Middle Billy Goat on the other side of the river! He is jumping up and down. I know they are fine, but what about me? Look at those huge bites of clover! I'm going, too!

Wind: Whoooooooooo! Whooooooooooooooo!

Big Billy Goat: Oh, no! The thing under the bridge will eat me!

Wind: Whoooooooooo! Whooooooooooooooo!

Big Billy Goat: It does sound a lot like the wind.

Wind: Whoooooooooo! Whooooooooooooooo!

Big Billy Goat: I see them waving to me again! They must be welcoming me to the other side of the bridge!

Wind: Whoooooooooo! Whooooooooooooooo!

Big Billy Goat: Good-bye, Wind! I'm off to get some clover!

All Billy Goats: Hurray! We are all together again.

Little Billy Goat: The clover tastes great!

Wind: Whoooooooooo! Whooooooooooooooo!

Big Billy Goat: I think the wind wants some, too!

Name _____

▶ **Read the story. Write three details about it.**

Last summer, Sara's family went to Washington, D.C., the capital of our country. They wanted to see all of the famous places they had read about. They saw the White House. They saw lots of statues. Sara's favorite part was going to the museums. She saw some items that belonged to Presidents. She even saw a real dinosaur skeleton! She can't wait to go back again.

_____

_____

_____

_____

_____

_____

_____

_____

School–Home Connection
Have your child recall a trip your family has
made. Talk about details of the trip.

Practice Book
© Harcourt • Grade 1 • Book 5

Name _____

Comprehension:
Main Idea
· · · · · · · ·
Theme 6
Cumulative
Application

▶ **Read the story. Circle the sentence that tells the main idea of the story.**

1. My aunt and I go bird watching on Saturdays. It is a lot of fun. We go to the park near my house. Many kinds of birds live there. Each makes a different sound. My aunt points to each bird and tells me its name. I learn a lot about birds from watching them with my aunt.

I like watching birds with my aunt.

Many birds live near my house.

---

2. Max's class took a trip to New York City. They saw many symbols of the country and the city. They visited the Statue of Liberty. Max liked riding the boat out to Liberty Island. He learned that the statue had been built by a man in France and given to the city as a gift. Max had a great time on the trip.

Max enjoyed his trip to New York City.

A man in France built the Statue of Liberty.

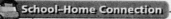
School-Home Connection
Read each story with your child. Together, think
of a good title for each one. Choose a title that
tells what the story is mainly about.

62

Name _____

▶ **Look at the pictures and read the sentences. Complete the sentence that follows. Tell how Josh and Emma are alike.**

Josh likes to play sports.
He is a fast runner.
He can't bat well.

Emma likes to play sports, too.
She is a good batter.
She can't run very fast.

_____
- -

I. Josh and Emma both like _____

_____
- -
_____

▶ **Now tell how Josh and Emma are different.**

_____
- -

2. Josh _____.

_____
- -

3. Emma _____.

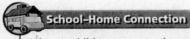
School-Home Connection

Ask your child to name another way that Josh
and Emma are different.

63

Practice Book
© Harcourt • Grade 1 • Book 5

Index

COMPREHENSION

GRAMMAR

Practice Book
© Harcourt • Grade 1

HIGH-FREQUENCY WORDS

PHONICS

Practice Book
© Harcourt • Grade 1

Practice Book
© Harcourt • Grade 1

Vowel Diphthong /ou/ow, *ou* **1-5:** 16, 18
Vowel Variant /o͞o/oo, *ew* **1-5:** 30, 32

SPELLING

1-1: 3, 10, 17, 24, 31, 38
1-2: 3, 10, 17, 24, 31, 38
1-3: 3, 10, 17, 24, 31, 38
1-4: 3, 10, 17, 24, 31, 38
1-5: 3, 10, 17, 24, 31, 38